INCREDIBLE

Dot-to-Dot

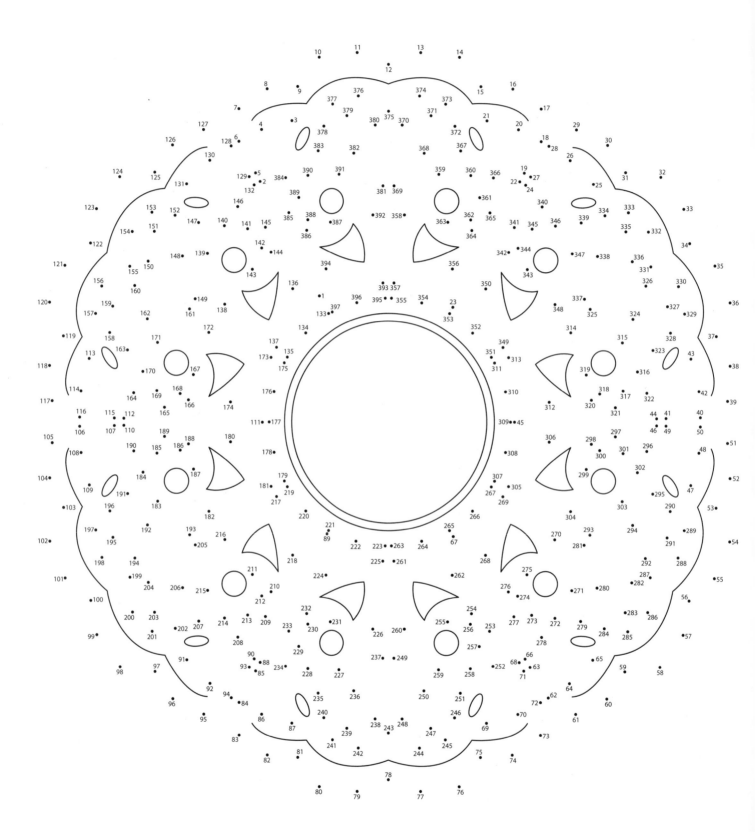

INCREDIBLE
Dot-to-Dot

DAVID WOODROFFE

ARCTURUS

NOTES:

Pictures made from 2 continuous lines -

Pg 8: a) 1 - 392 and b) a - g; **Pg 16:** a) 1 - 355 and b) a - m; **Pg 37:** a) 1 - 400 and b) a - u; **Pg 40:** a) 1 - 400 and b) a - p; **Pg 41:** a) 1 - 400 and b) a - g; **Pg 47:** a) 1 - 394 and b) a - q; **Pg 53:** a) 1 - 366 and b) a - x; **Pg 55:** a) 1 - 344 and b) a - j; **Pg 68:** a) 1 - 396 and b) a - p; **Pg 69:** a) 1 - 367 and b) a - t; **Pg 73:** a) 1 - 361 and b) a - z; **Pg 80:** a) 1 - 400 and b) a - v; **Pg 99:** a) 1 - 400 and b) a - l; **Pg 102:** a) 1 - 397 and b) a - j; **Pg 104:** a) 1 - 351 and b) a - s; **Pg 125:** a) 1 - 380 and b) a - l.

Pictures made from 3 continuous lines -

Pg 70: a) 1 - 357, b) A - M and c) a - t; **Pg 93:** a) 1 - 325, b) A - R and c) a - q ; **Pg 119:** a) 1 - 385, b) a - k and c) A - E.

Pictures made from 4 continuous lines -

Pg 77: a) 1 - 383, b) a - j, c) A - G and d) I - IV; **Pg 78:** a) 1 - 328, b) a - t, c) A - T and d) 1 - 38; **Pg 82:** a) 1 - 334, b) a - y, c) A - Z and d) I -XIV.

ARCTURUS

© 2016 Arcturus Holdings Limited

ISBN 978-1-78599-233-9
CH005042

Manufactured in China

2 4 6 8 10 9 7 5 3 1

CONTENTS

INTRODUCTION

Lots of dots, up to 400 of them on each page, and all you have to do is connect them in the sequence in which they are numbered. What could be easier? In truth it can prove more difficult than you would think—but only if you don't follow a few basic rules. The first is to be observant: The dots may be numbered in sequence but they may not always be positioned adjacent to each other, and it might take some careful searching for you to find the next one—and before you start anything you will need to locate number 1! Sometimes, a picture may contain more than one line. Check the notes on page 4 to identify these.

Subjects have been chosen because of their incredible size, appearance or reputation—from works of art and famous figures from history to awe-inspiring buildings, mythical creatures, and amazing machinery. The subjects will vary in difficulty—some will be incredibly easy, while others will take patience and a keen eye to complete.

All you need is a sharp pencil or pen and a straight edge to draw against for the long lines, and, hey presto, you have created an incredible image.

Start by trying this picture of a lovable seabird. I hope you'll find it an enjoyable warm-up exercise for the challenges ahead. Once you've completed it, you'll soon be connecting dots on the big pictures like a professional!

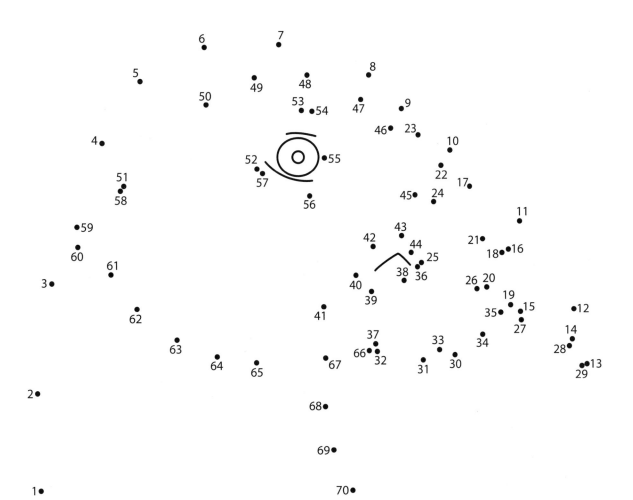

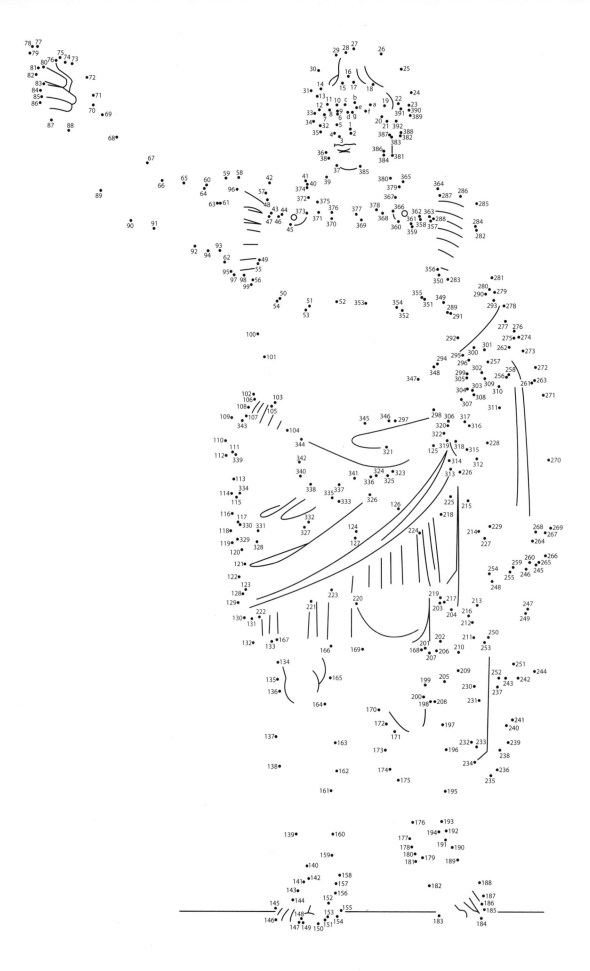

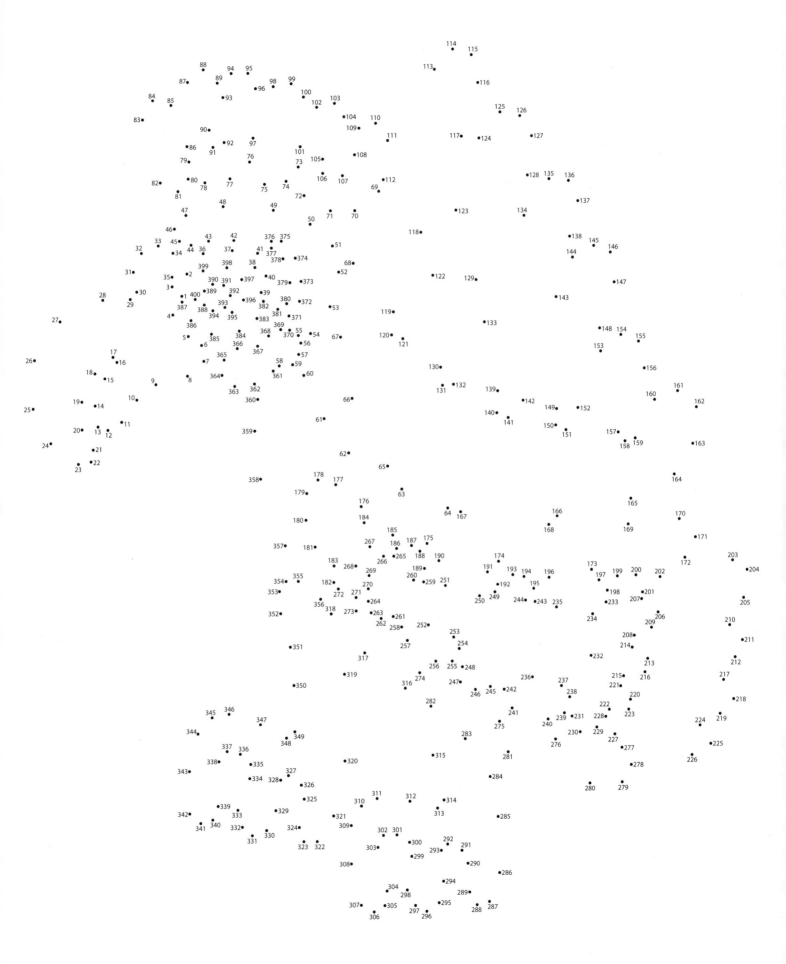

13

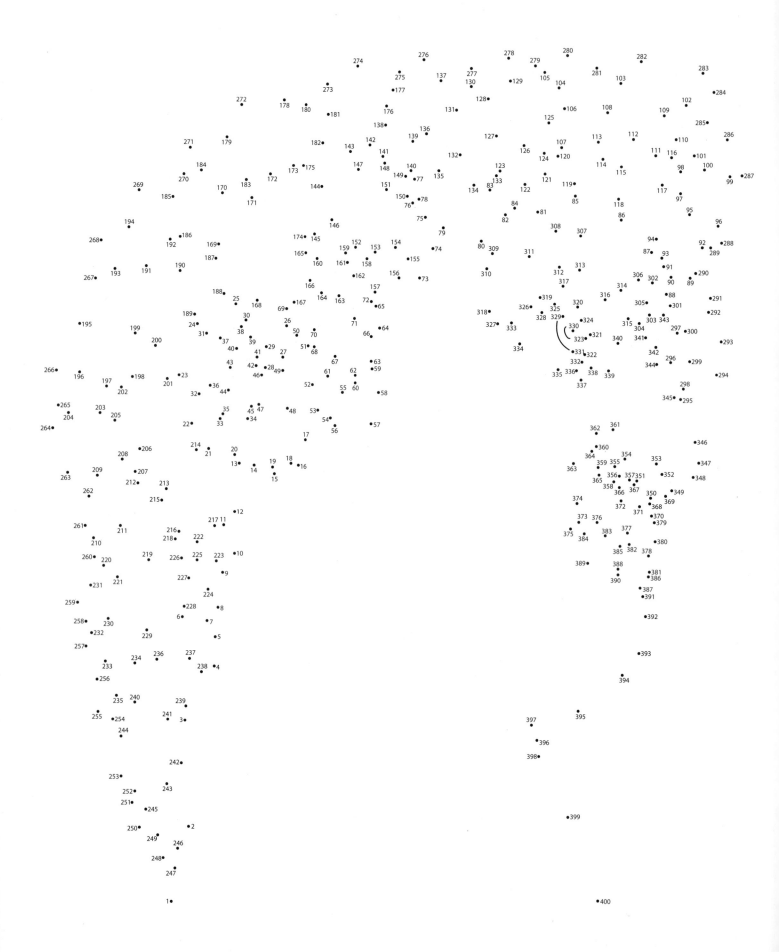

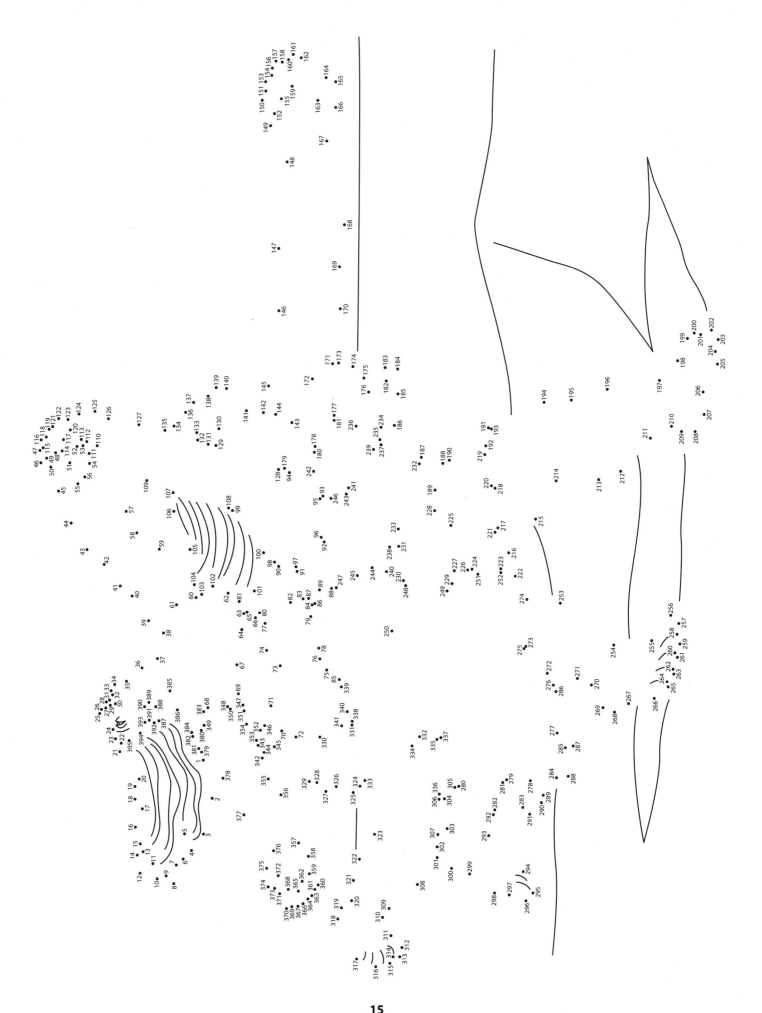

15

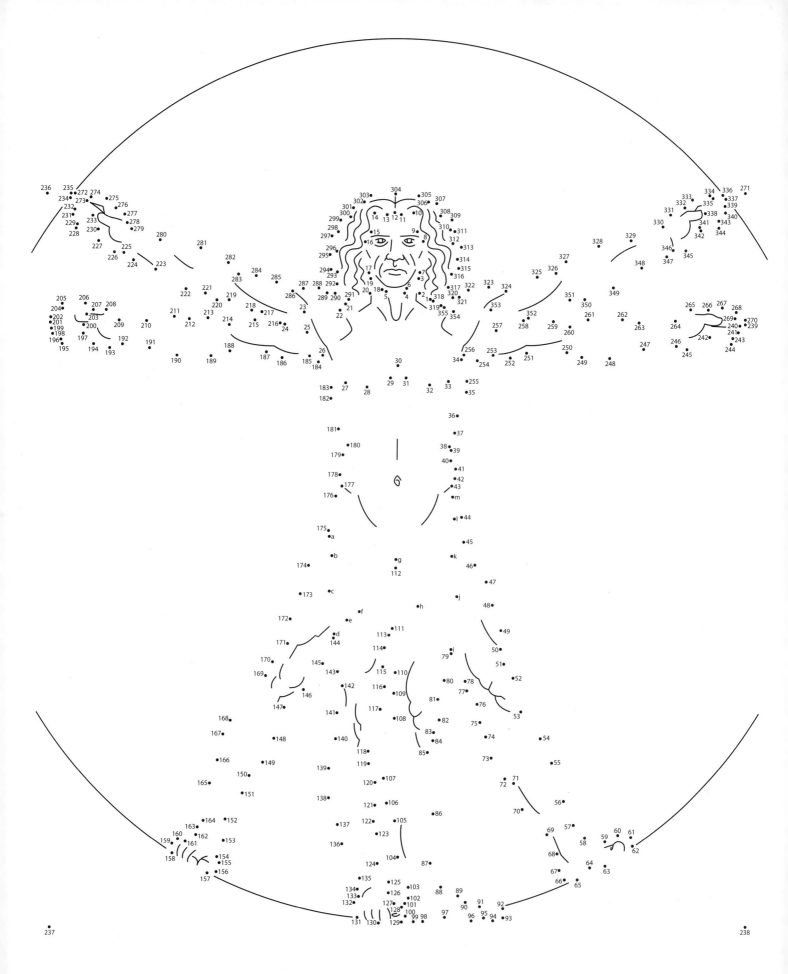

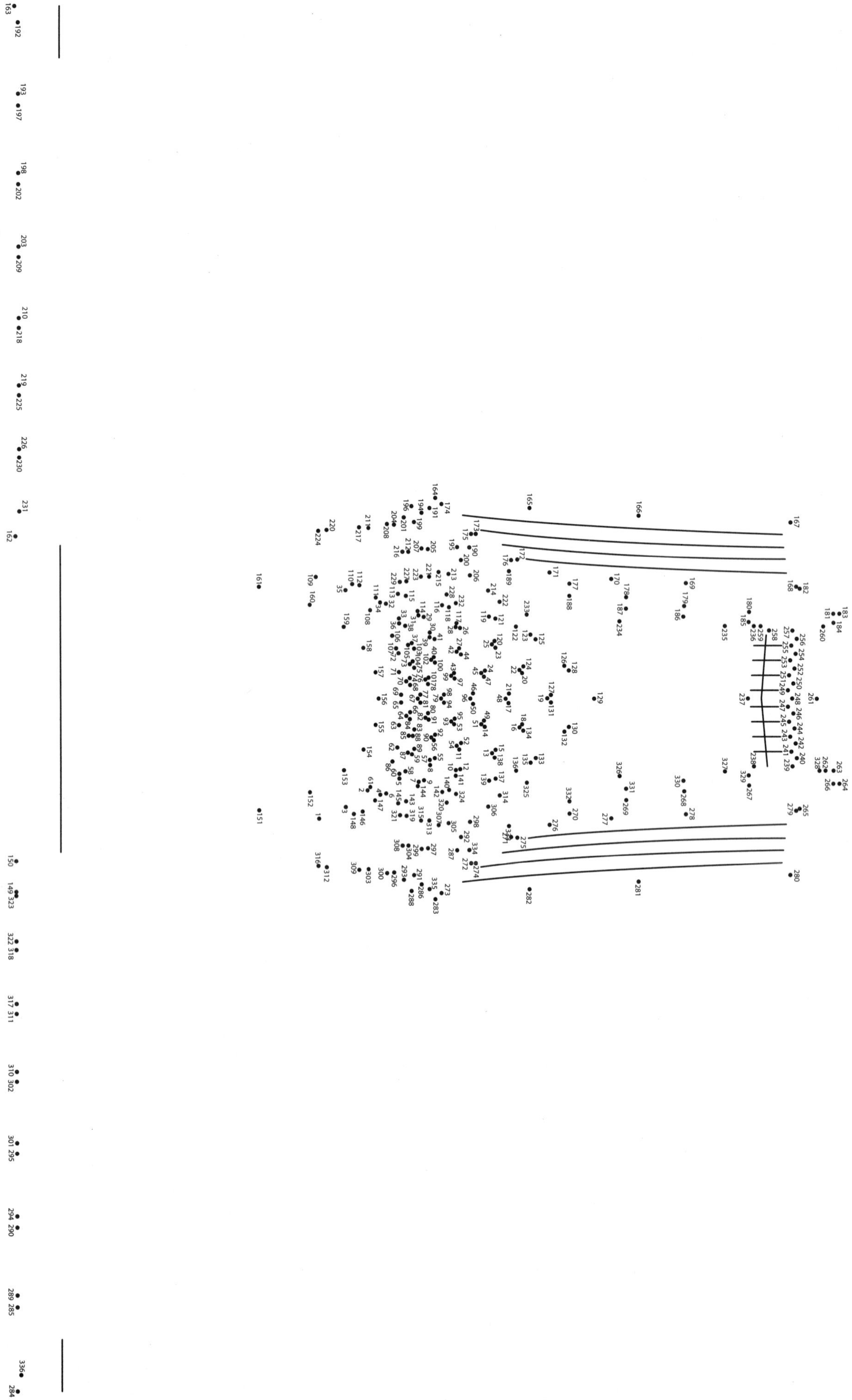

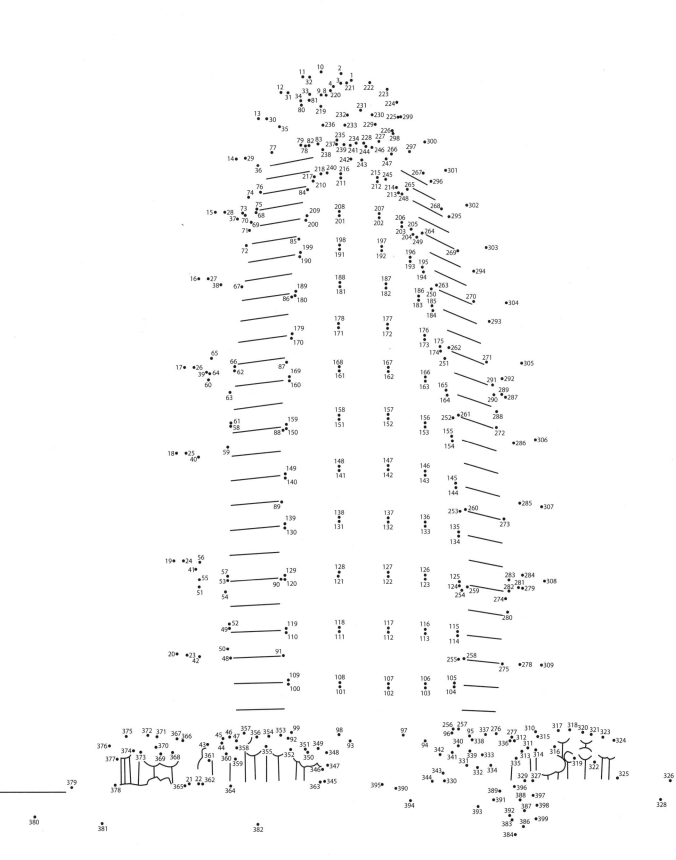

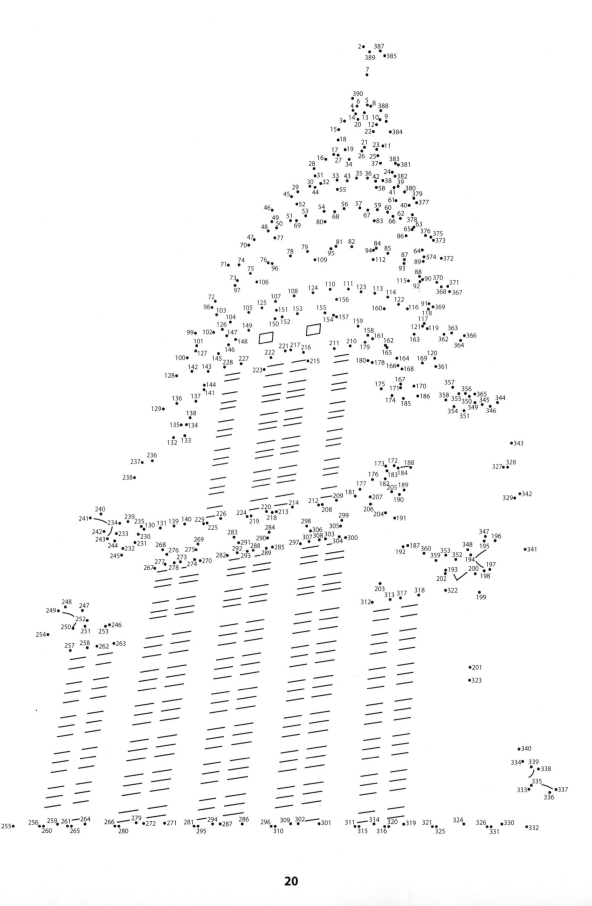

20

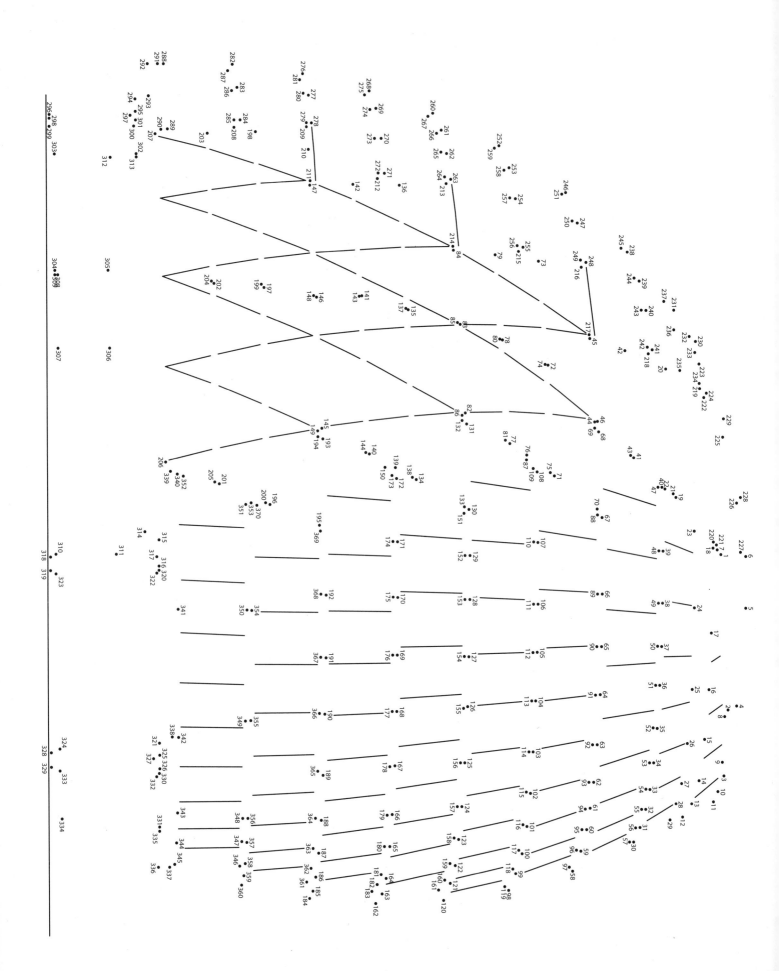

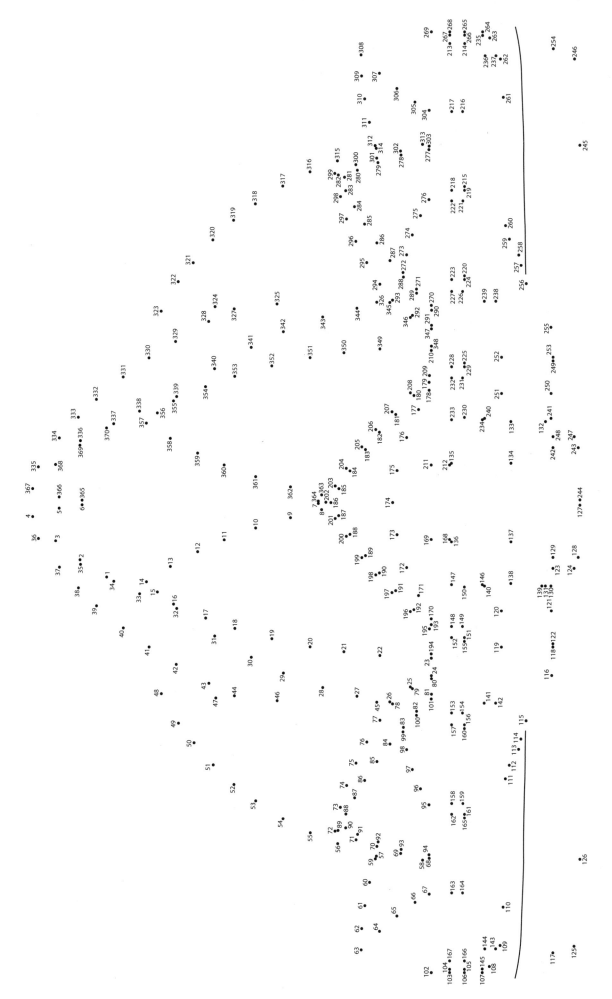

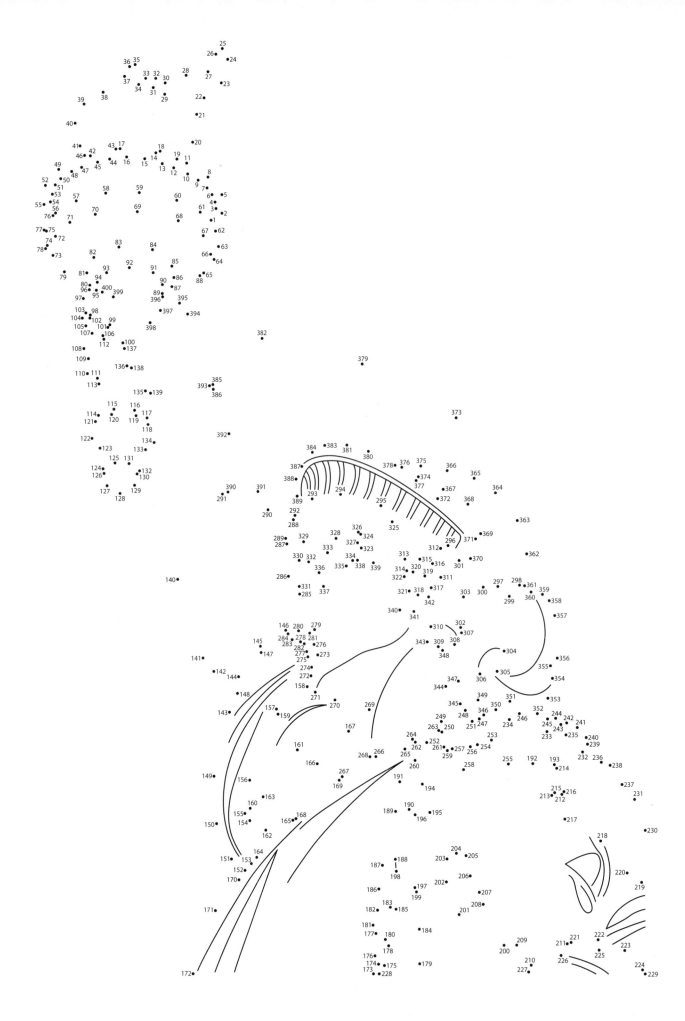

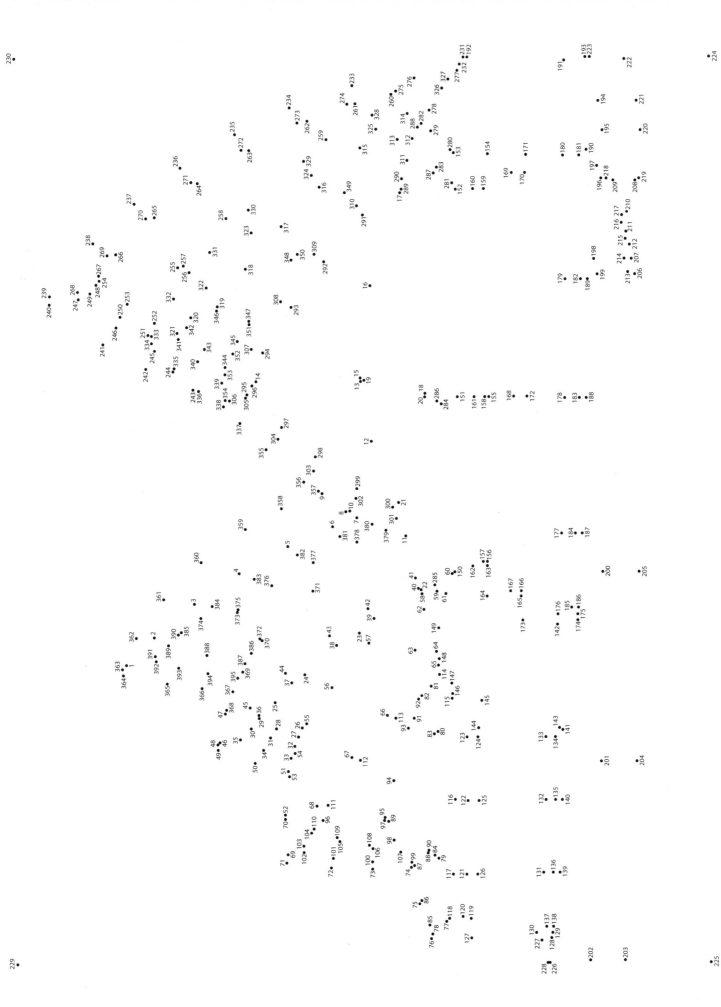

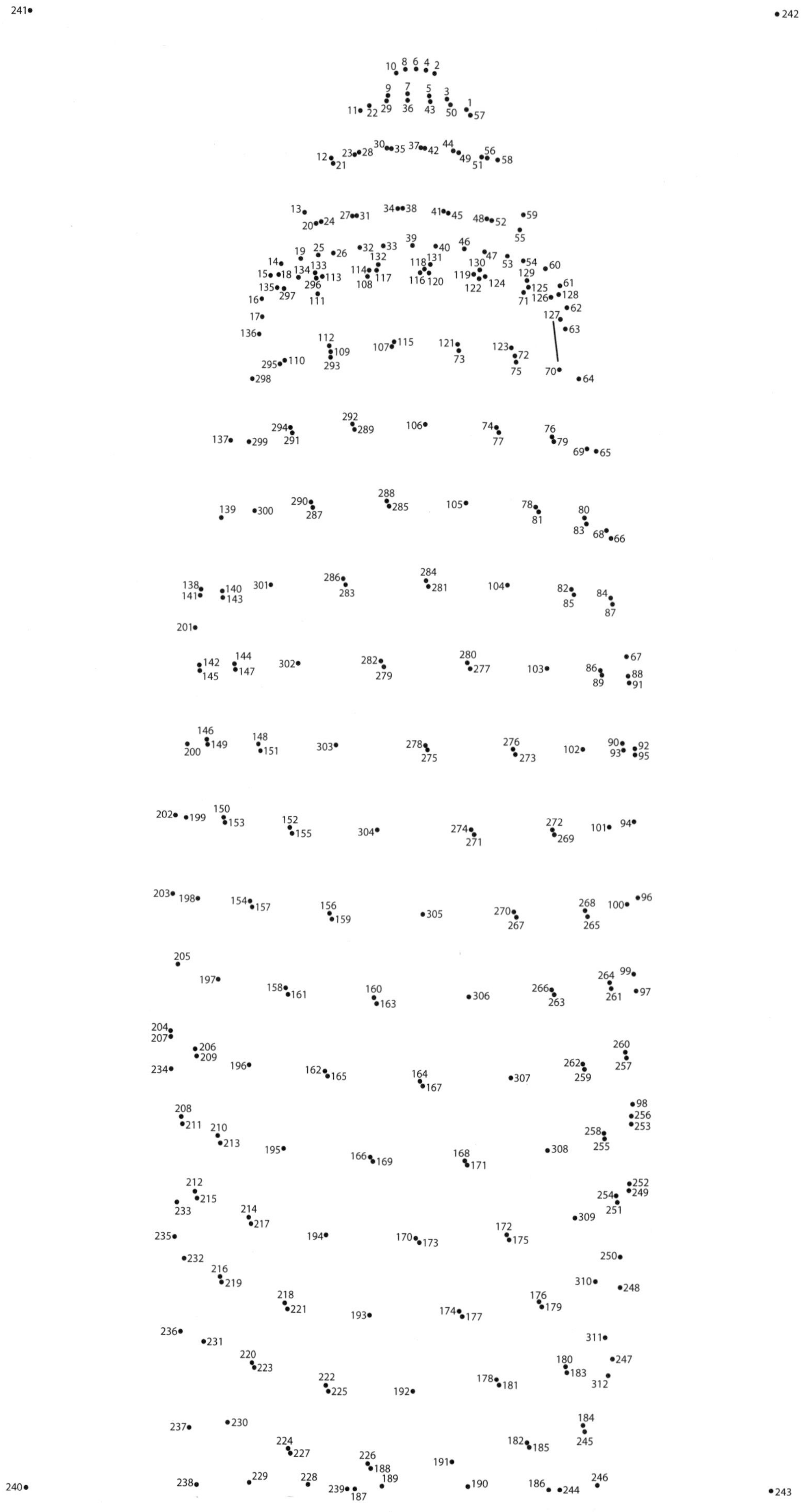

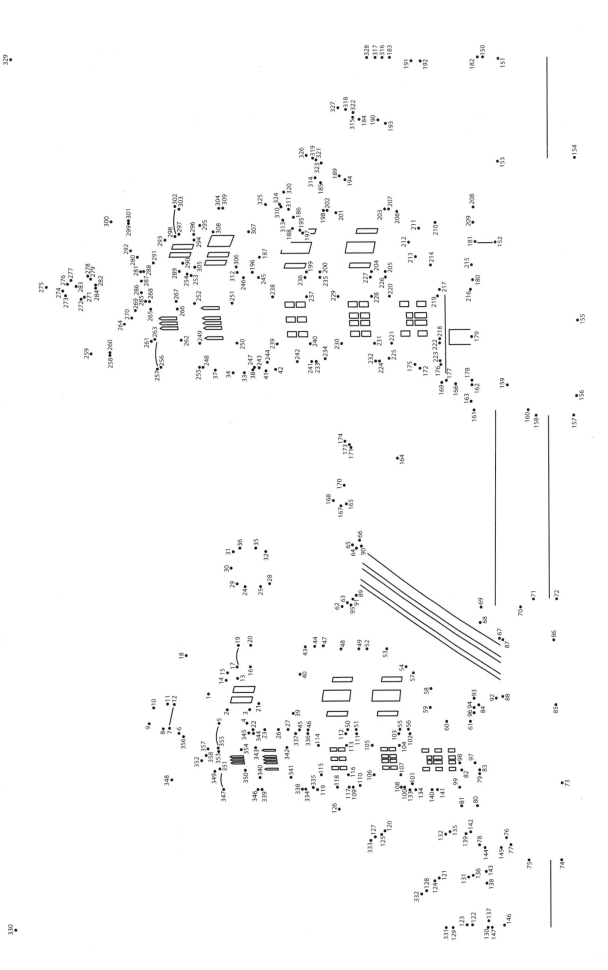

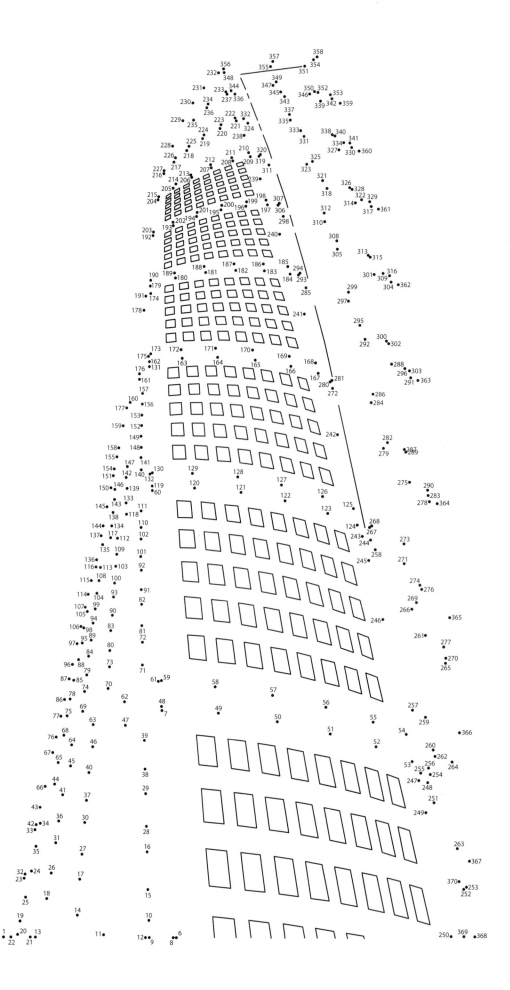

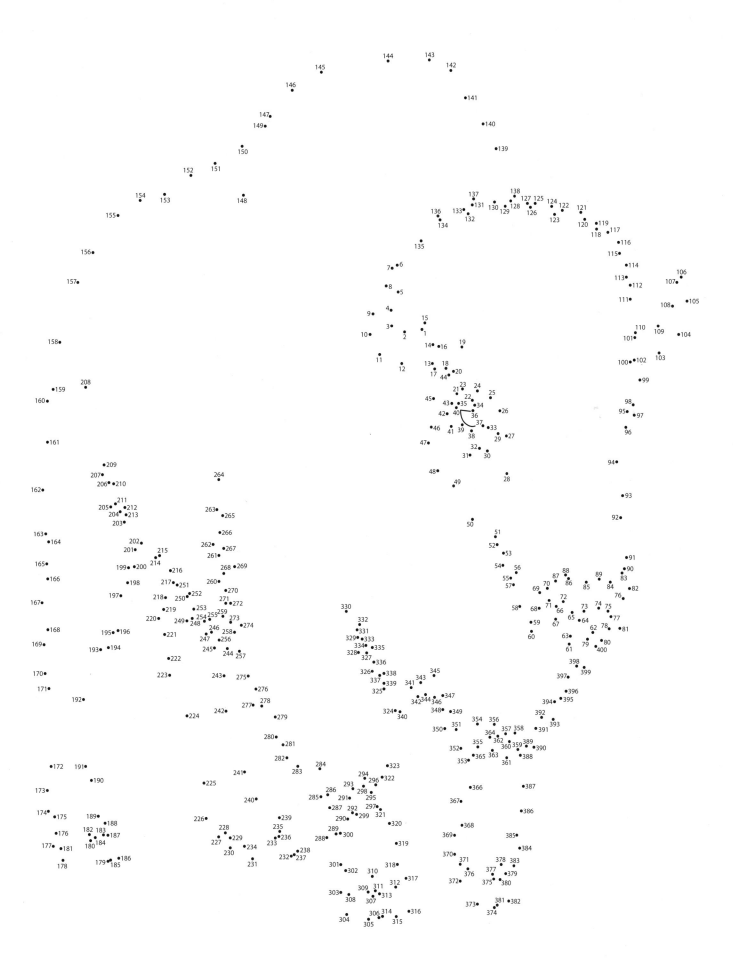

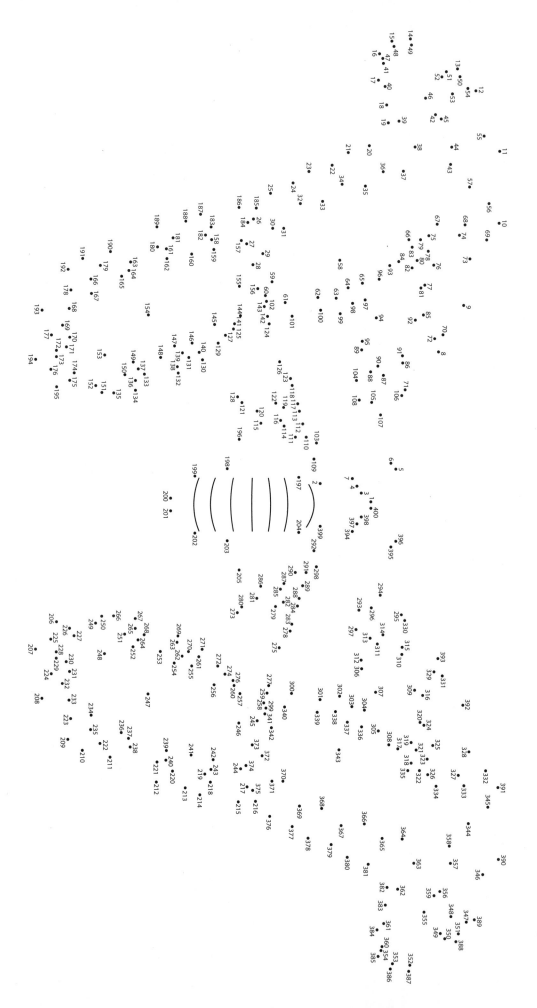

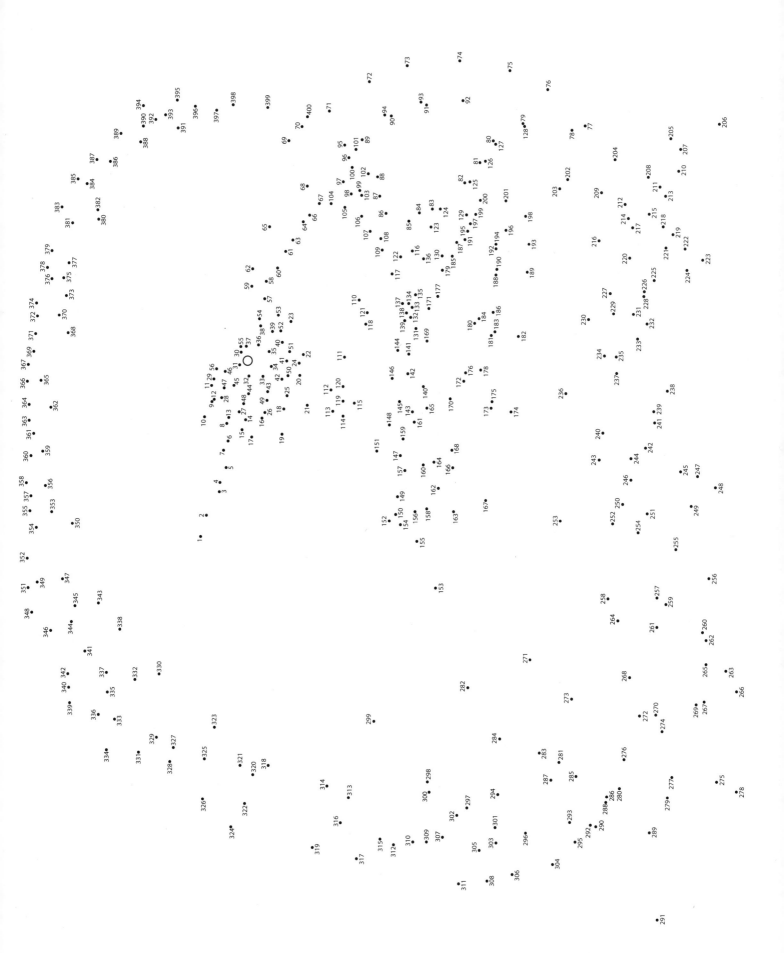

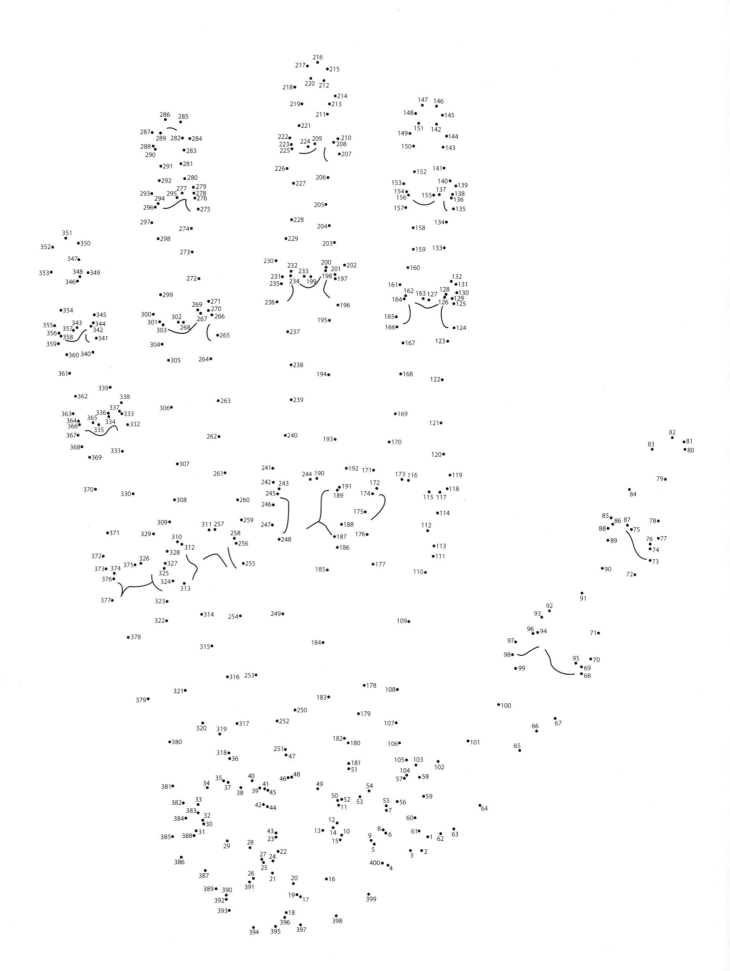

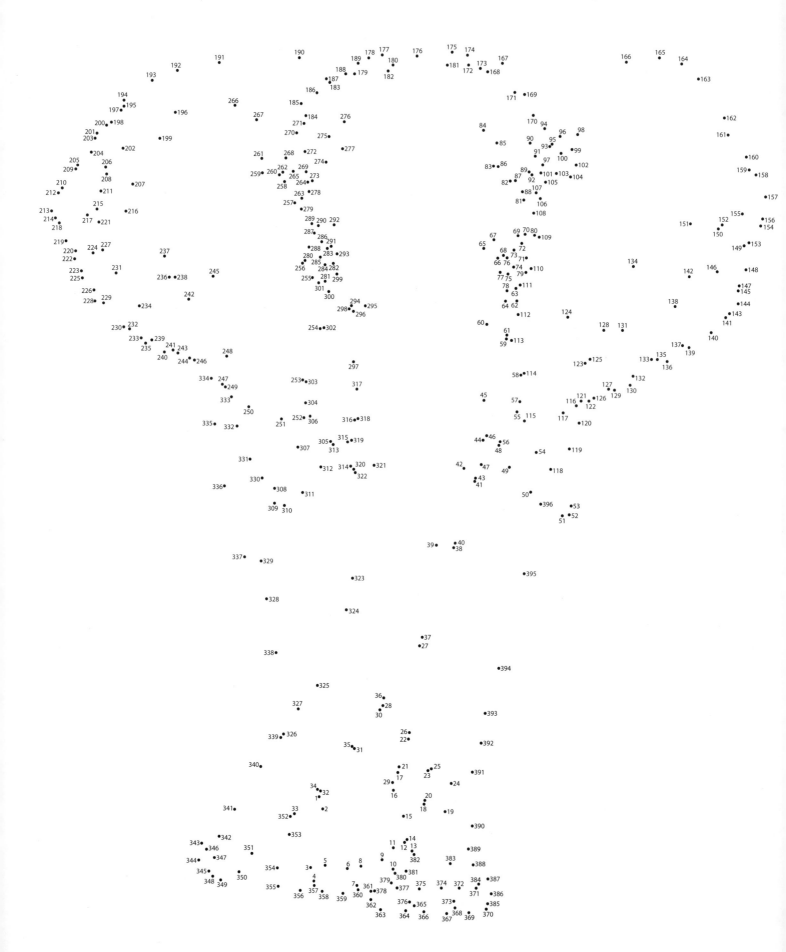

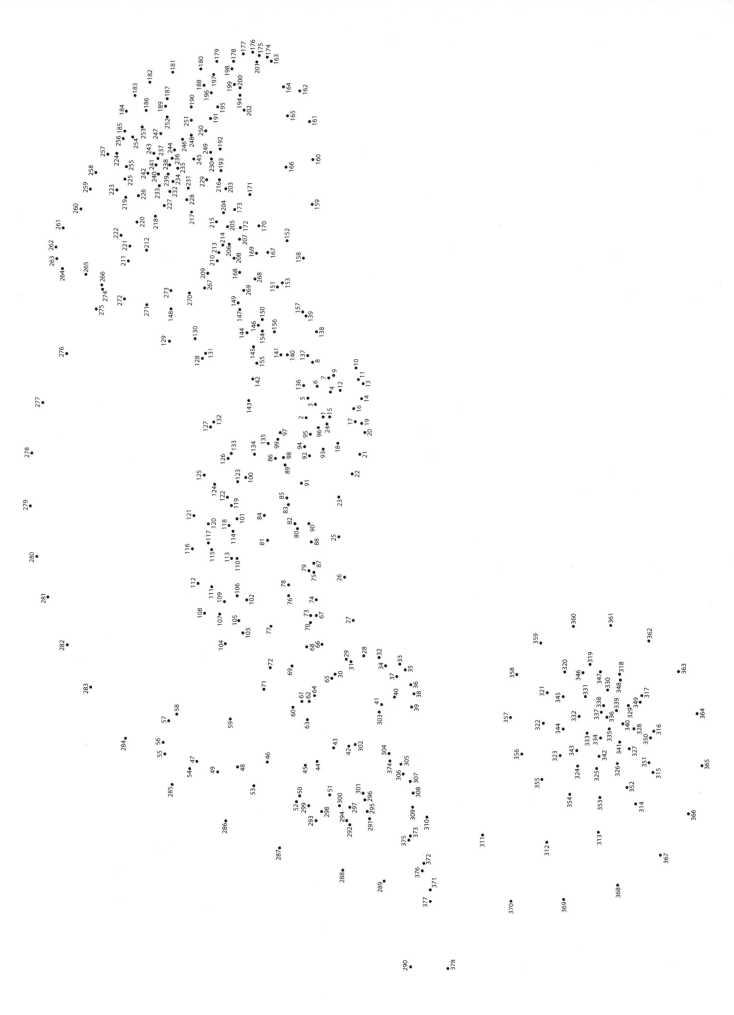

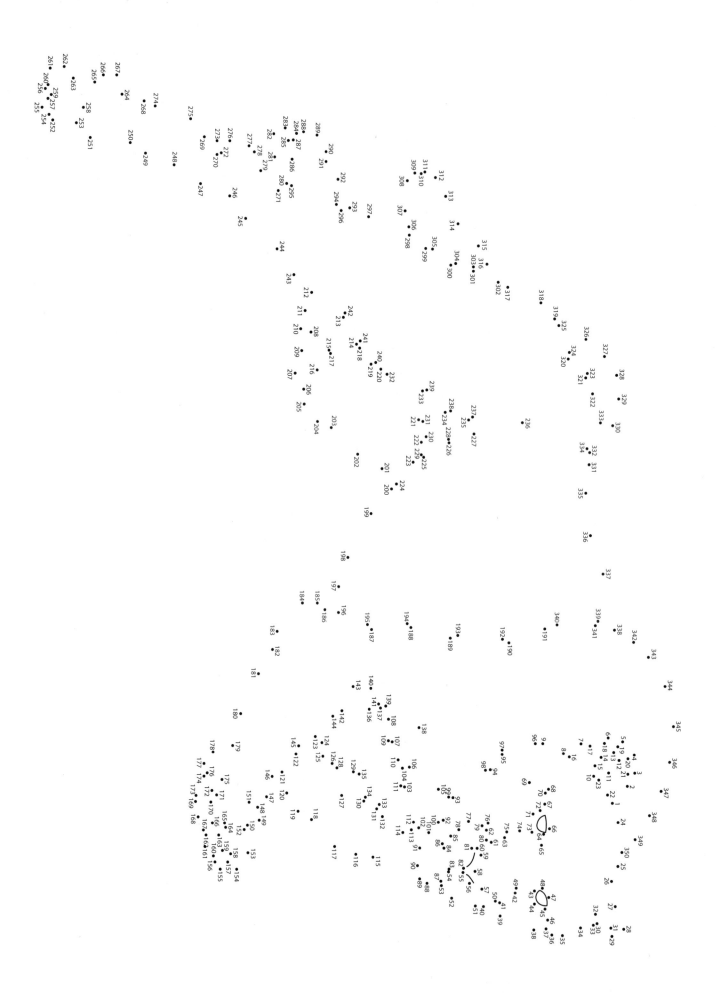

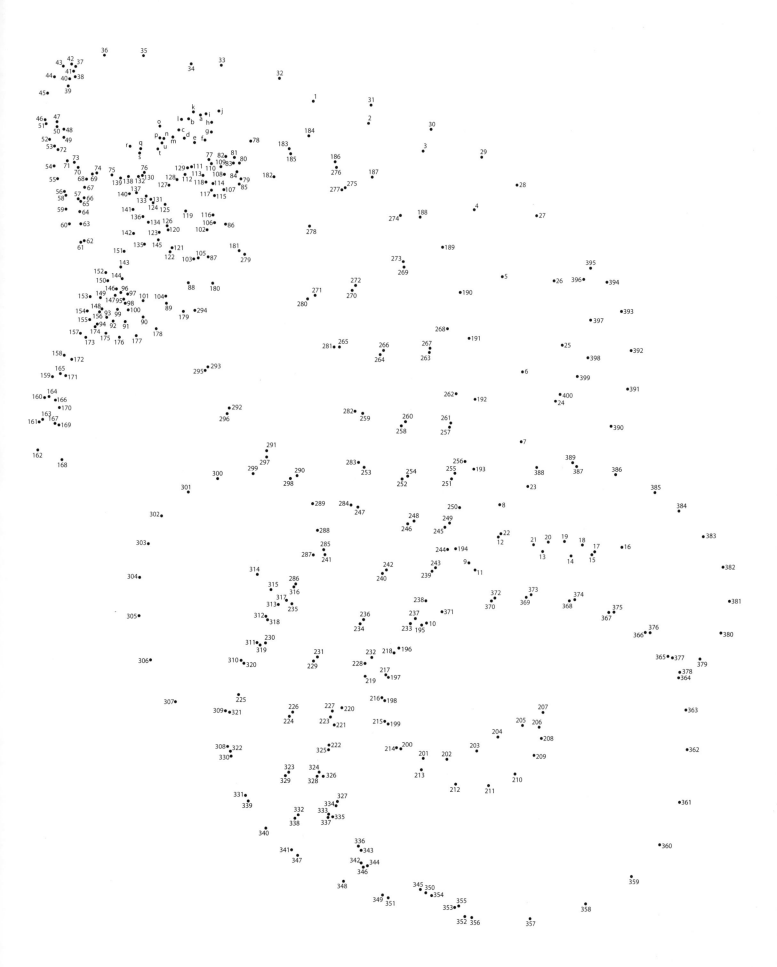

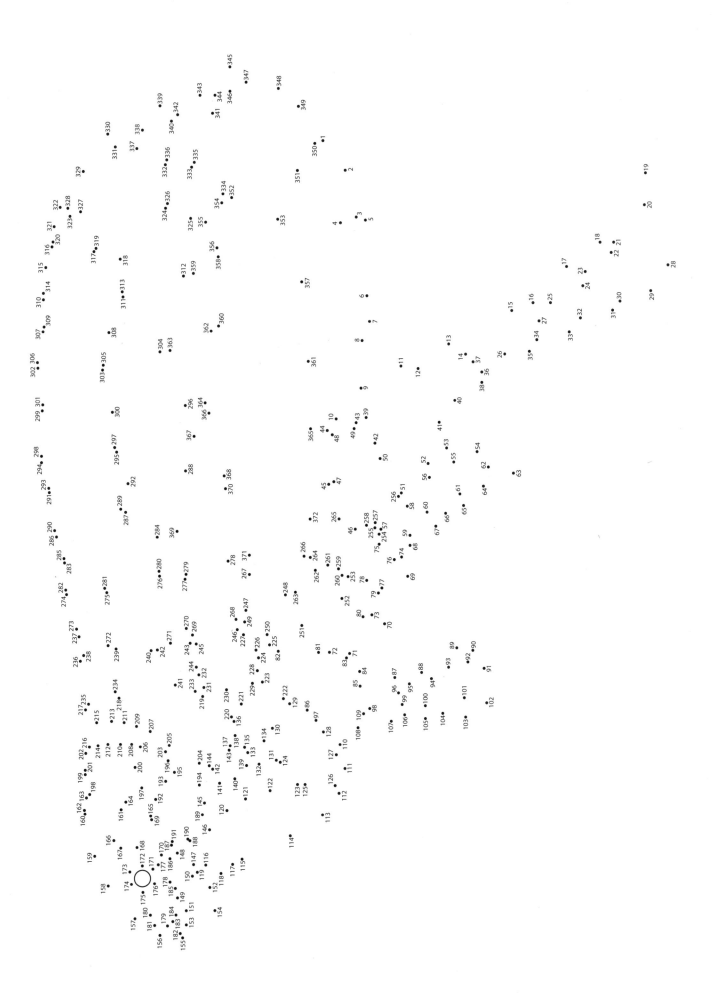

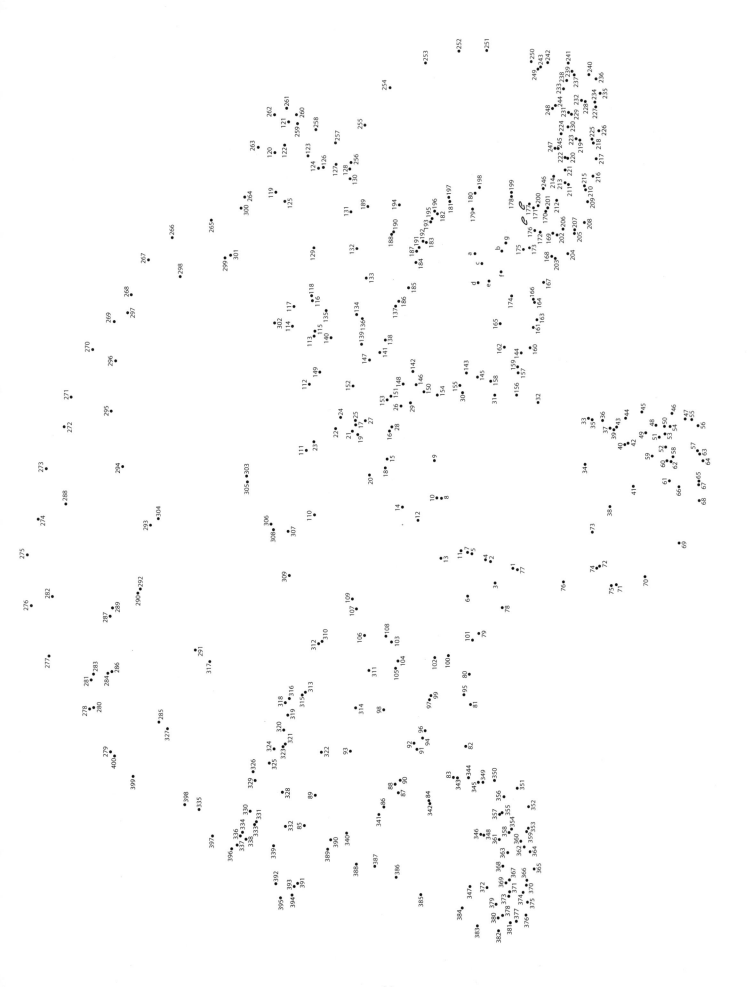

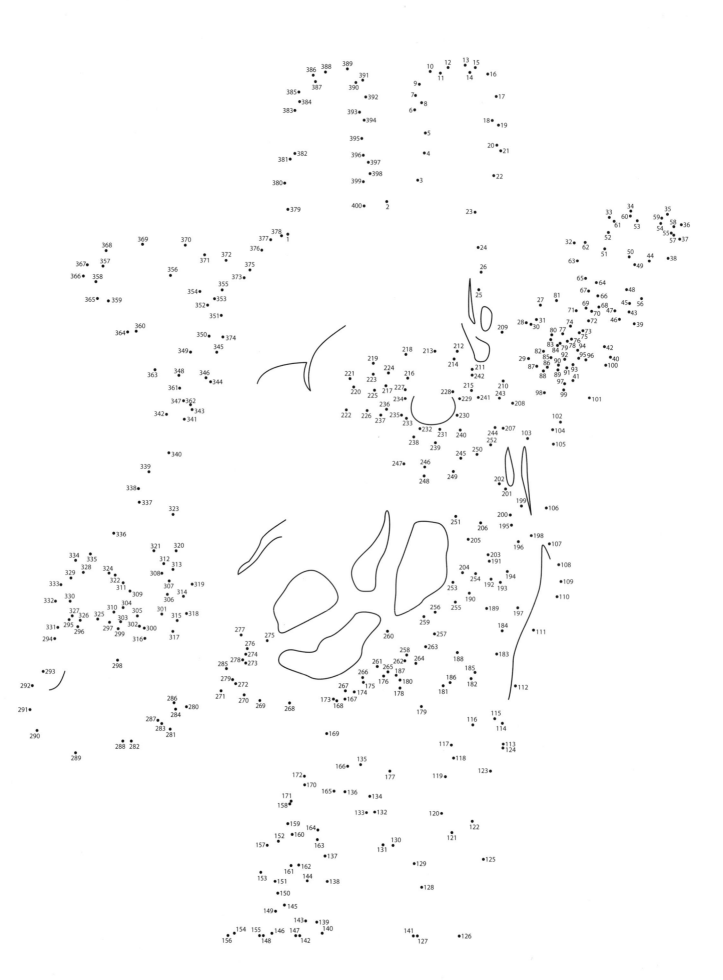

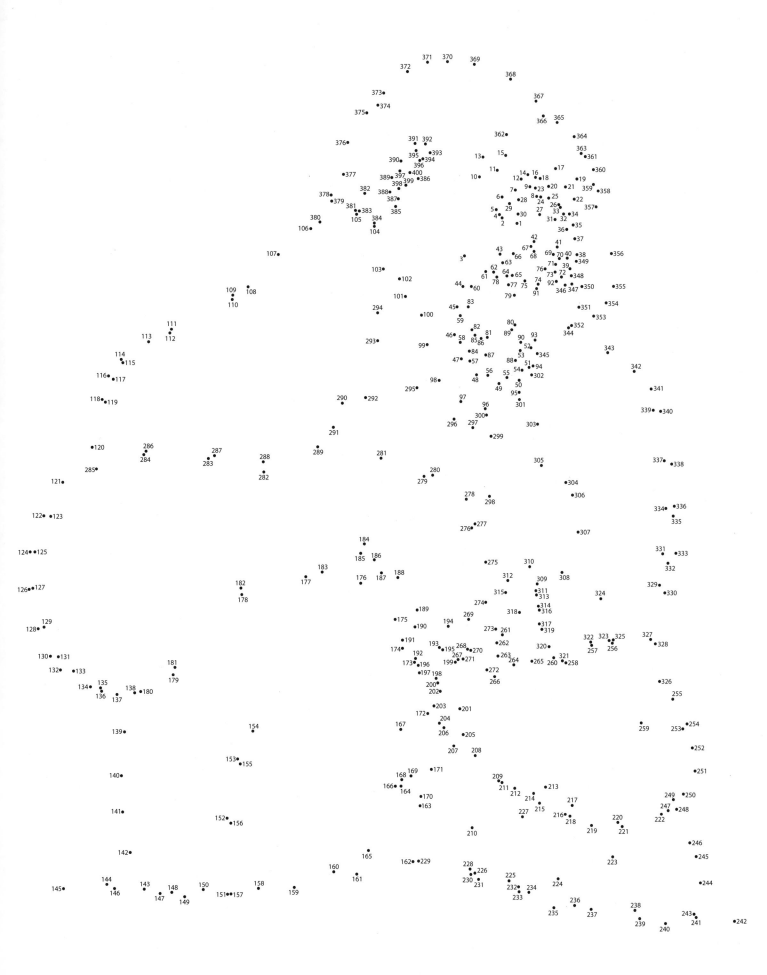

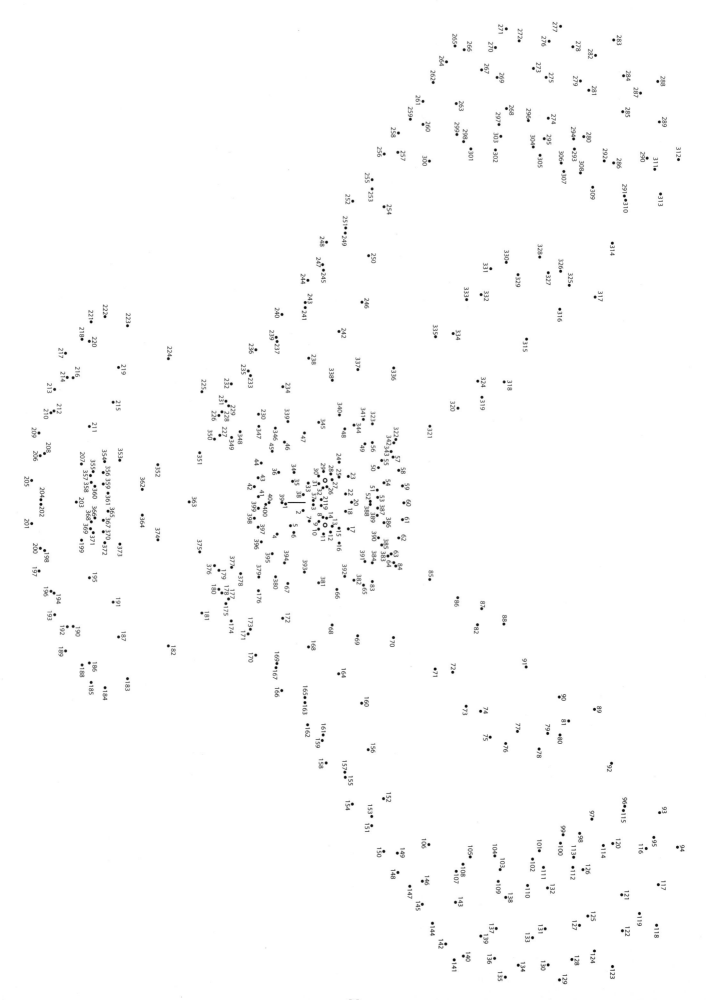

44

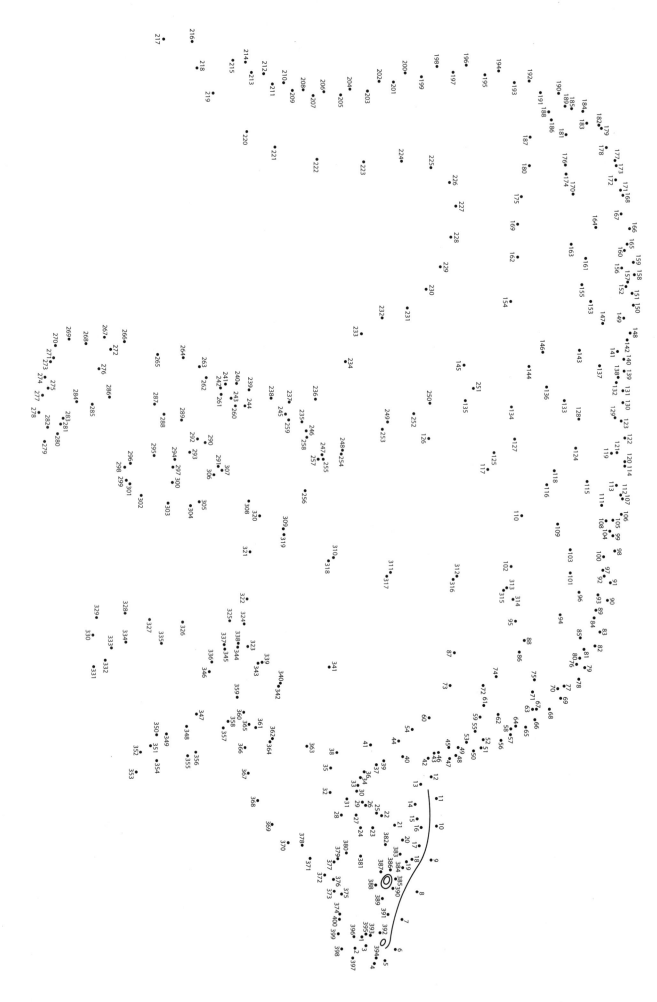

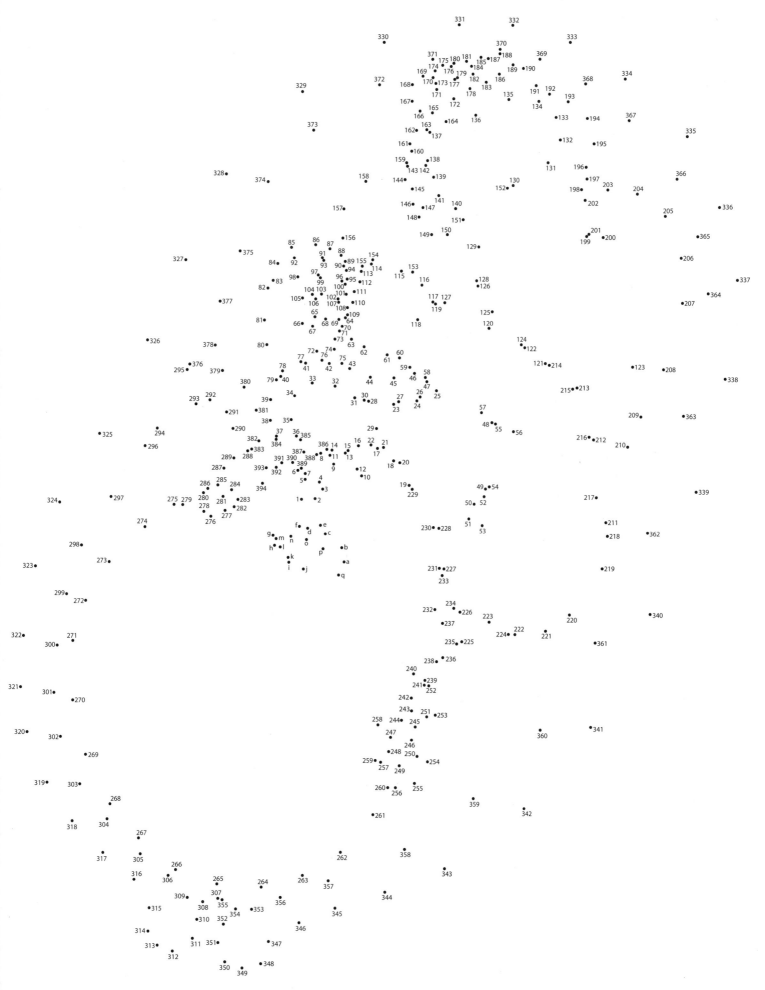

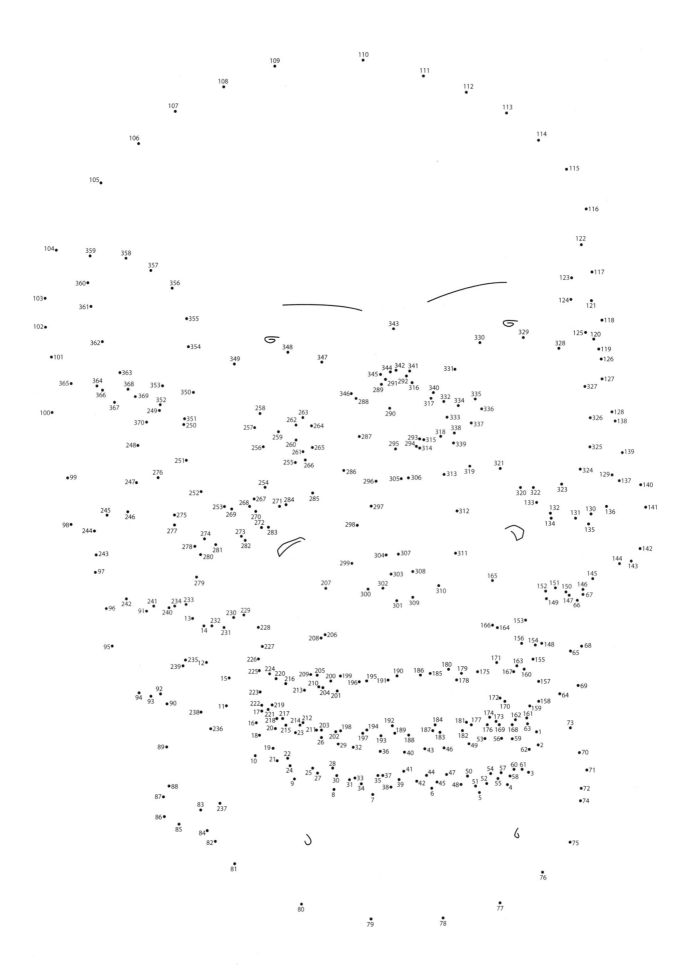

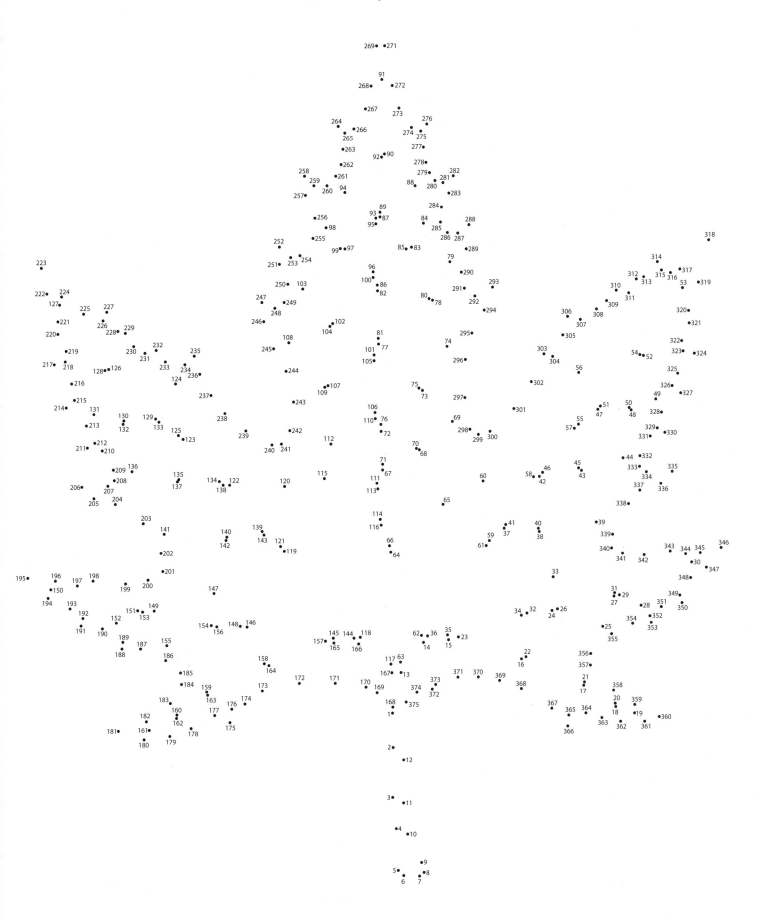

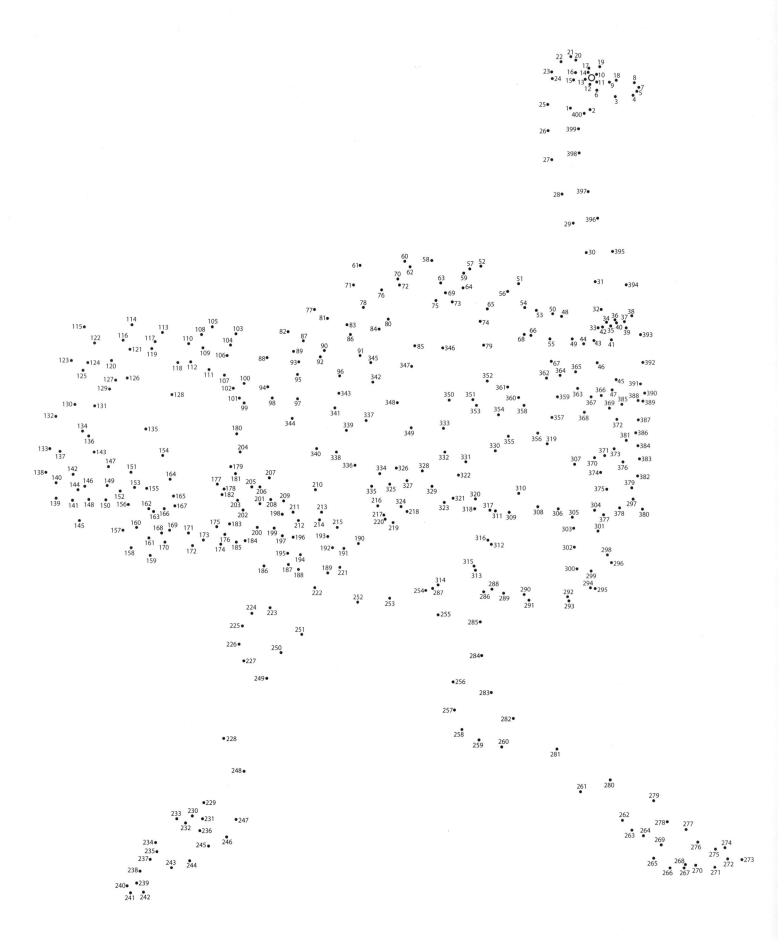

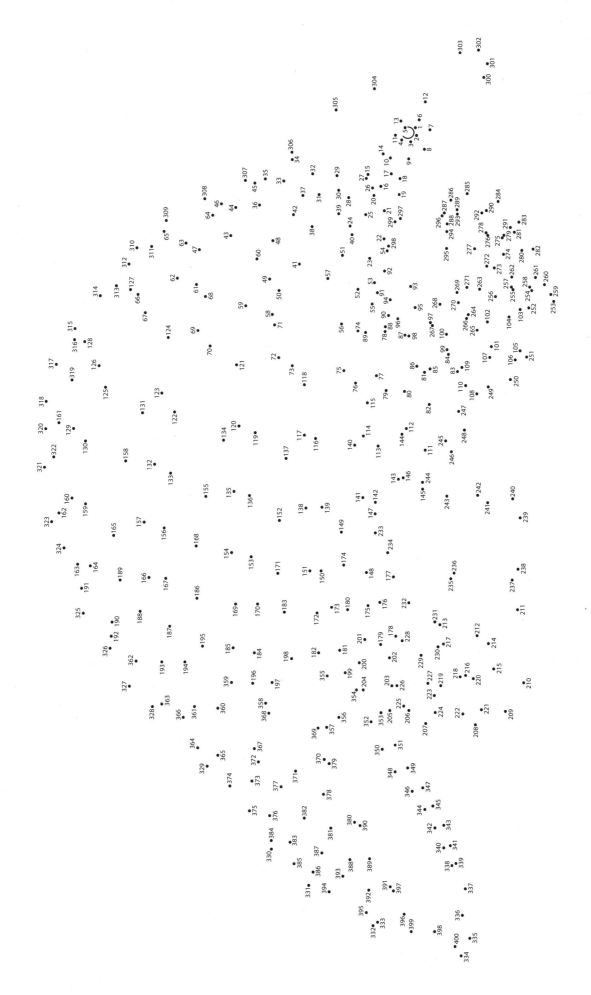

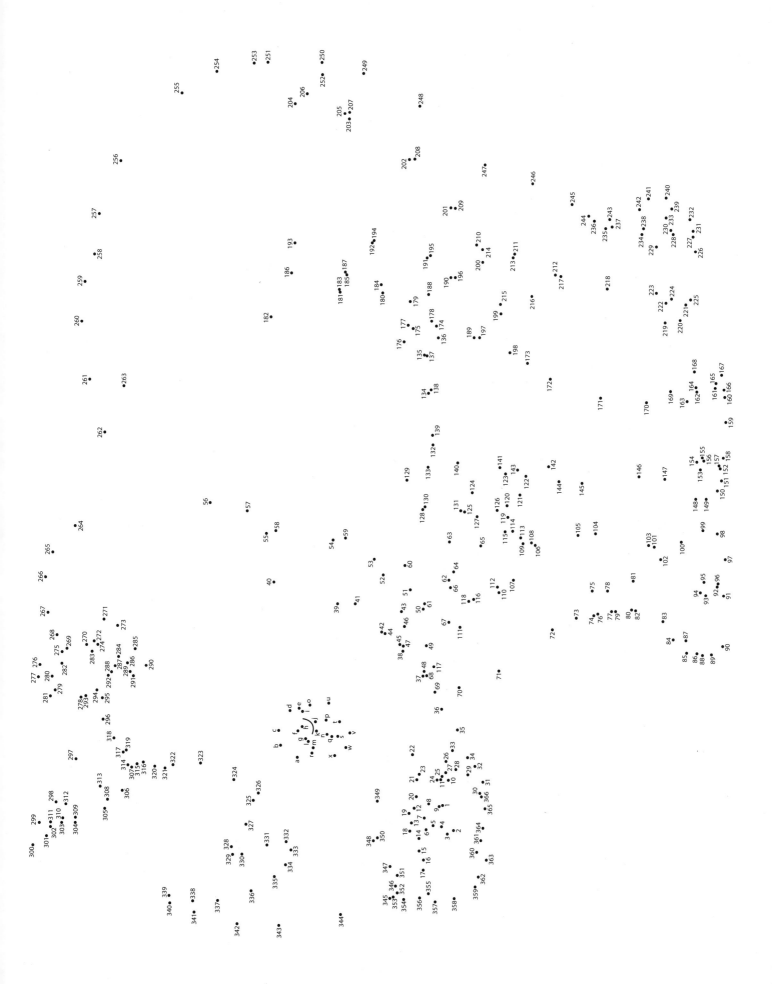

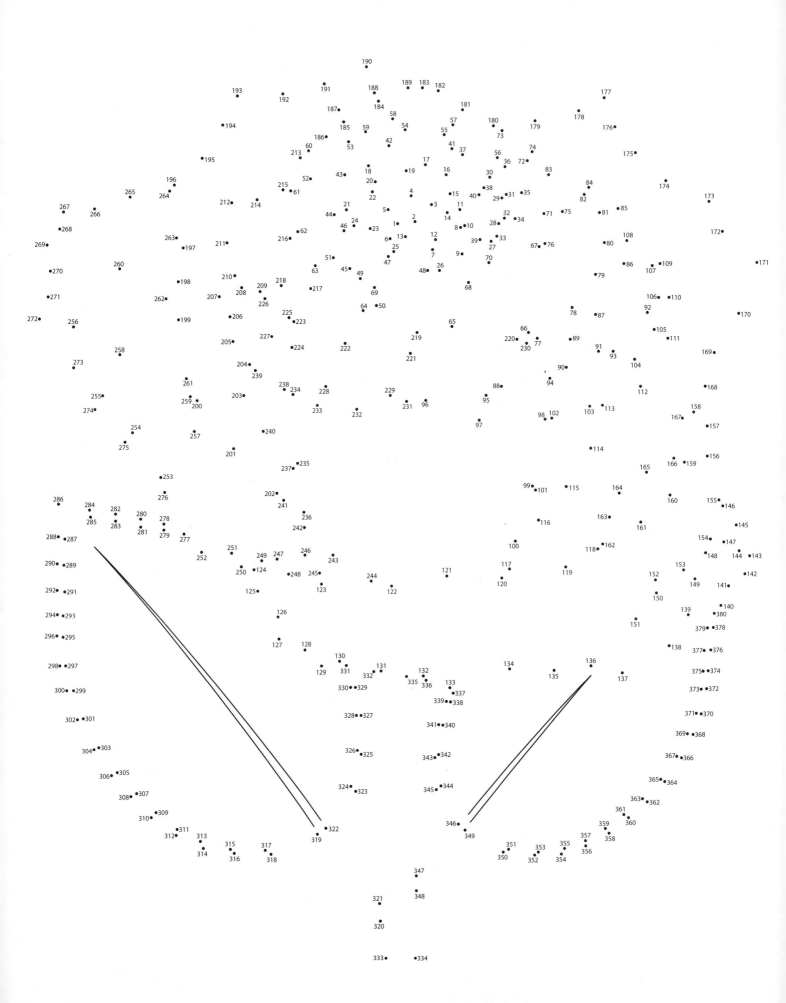

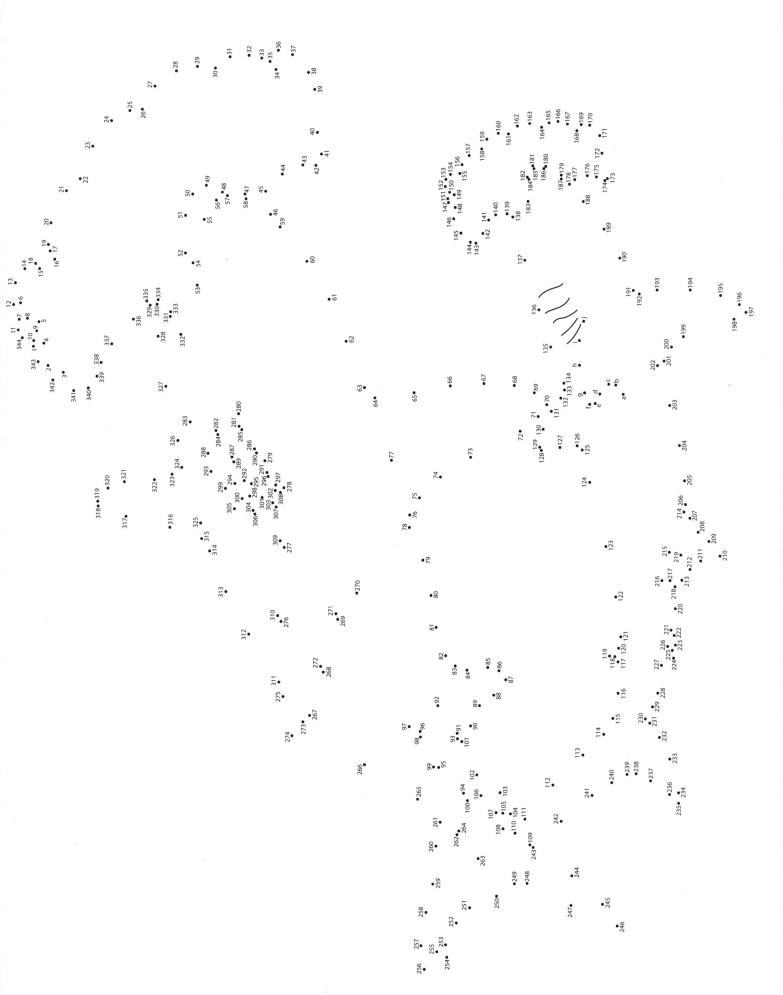

55

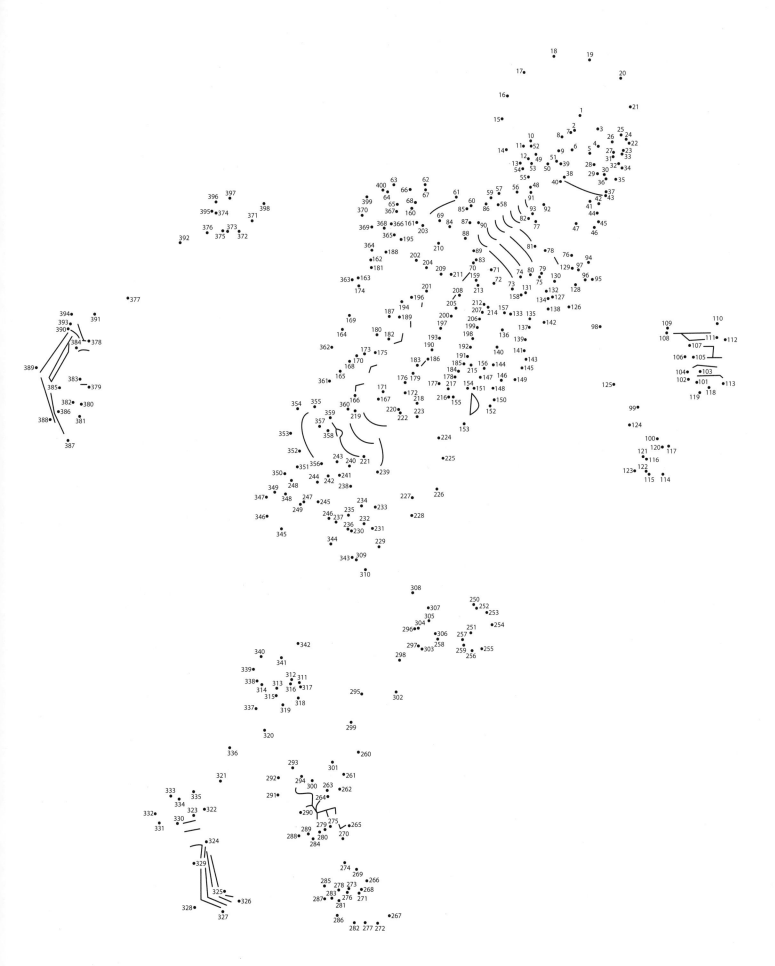

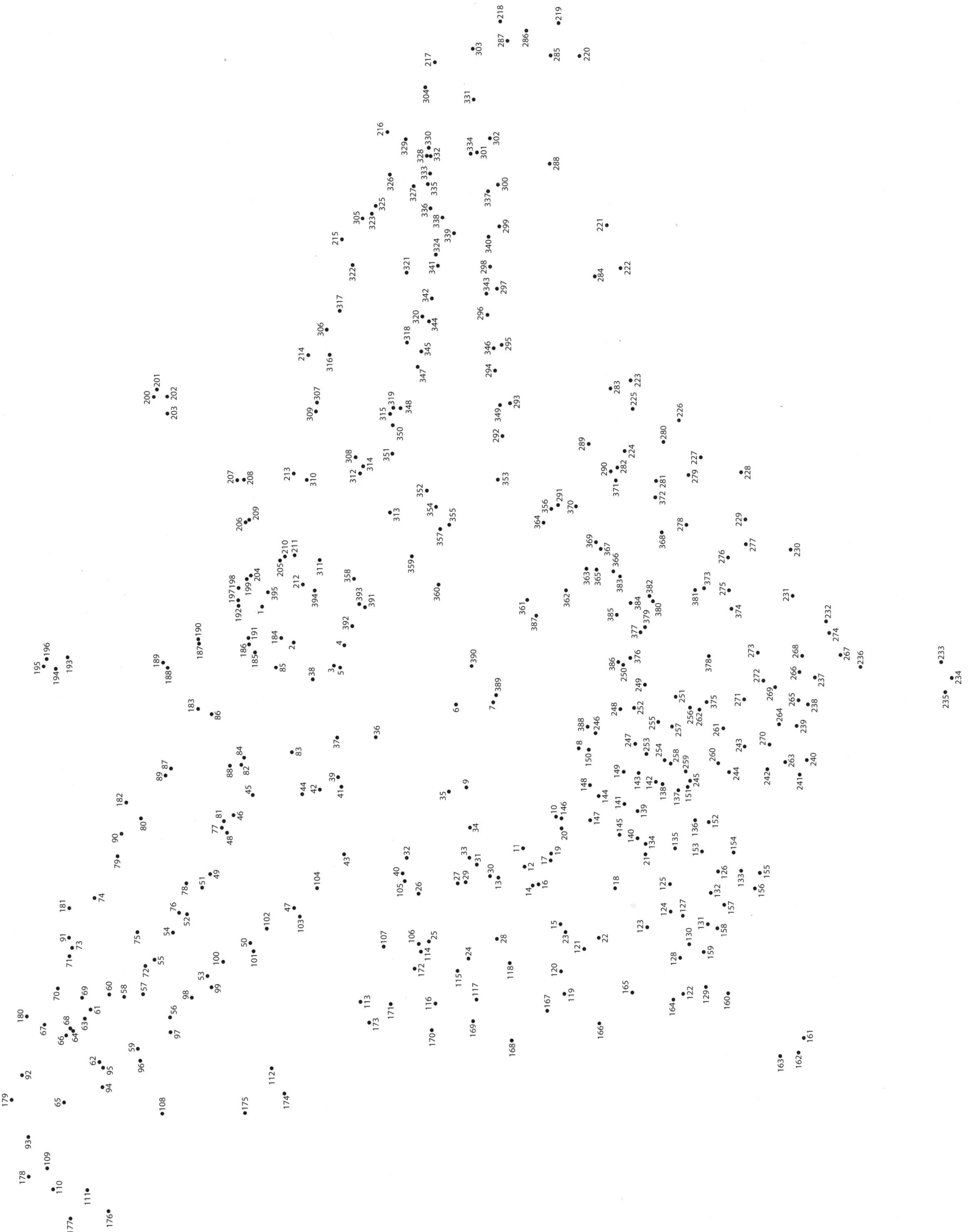

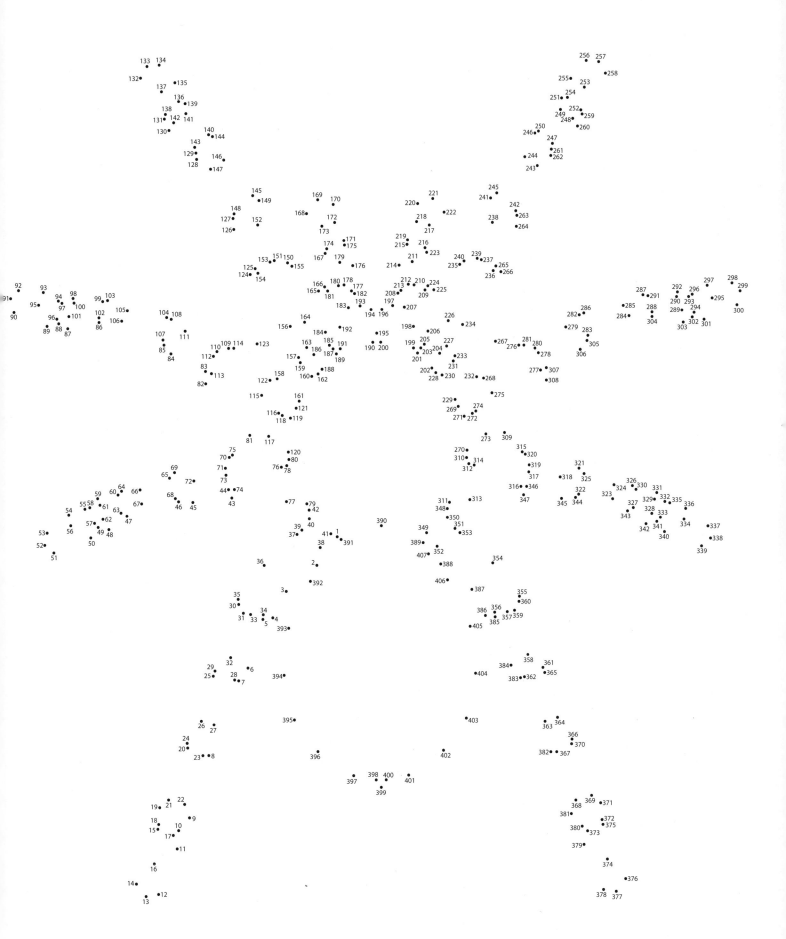

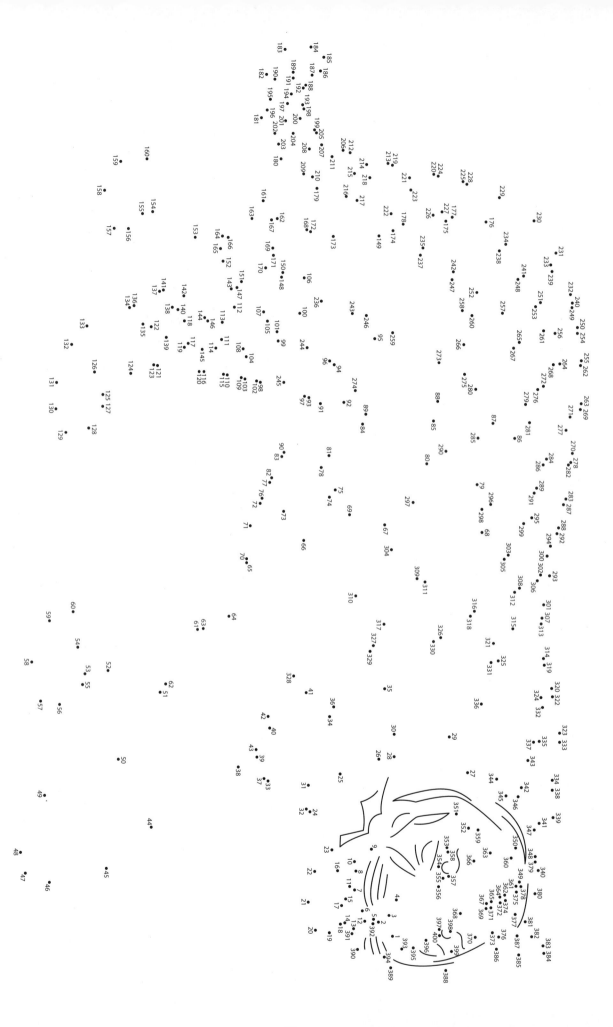

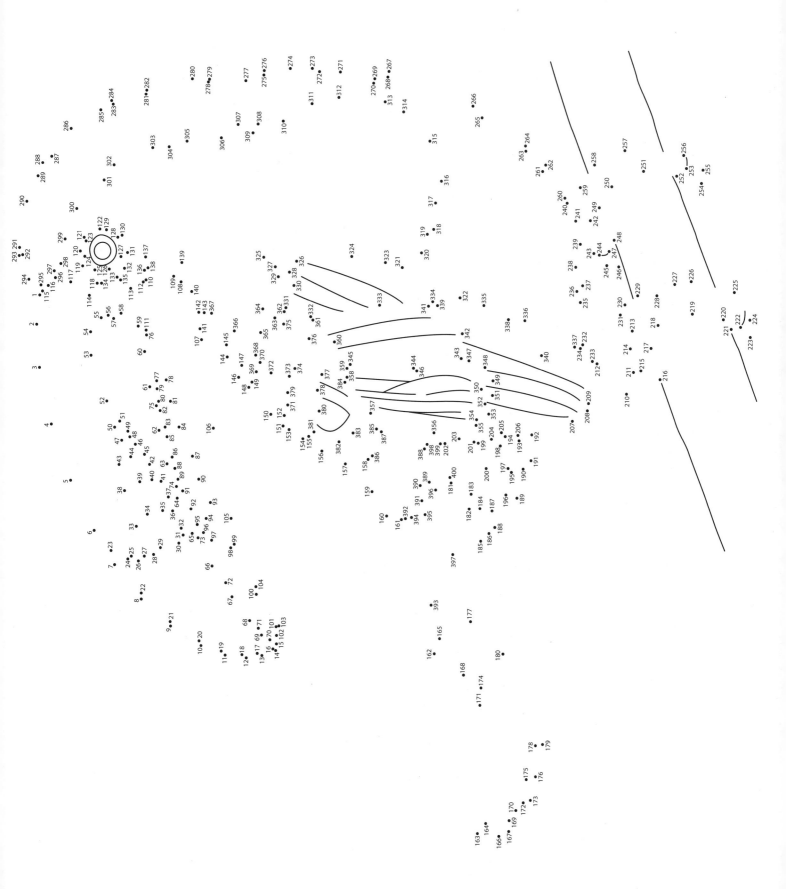

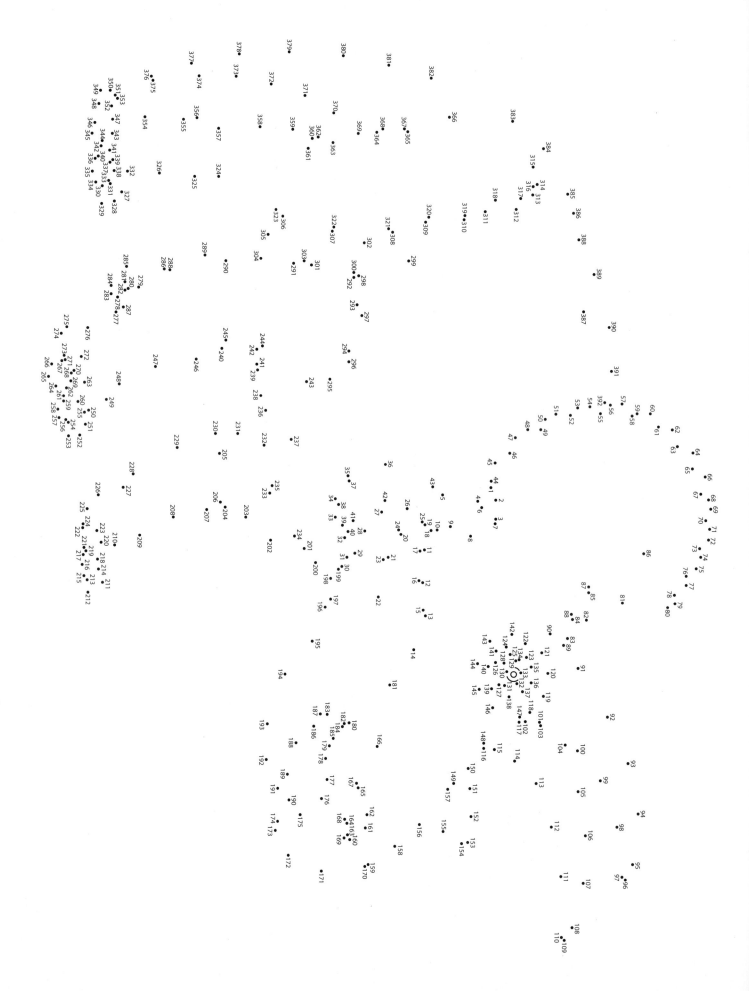

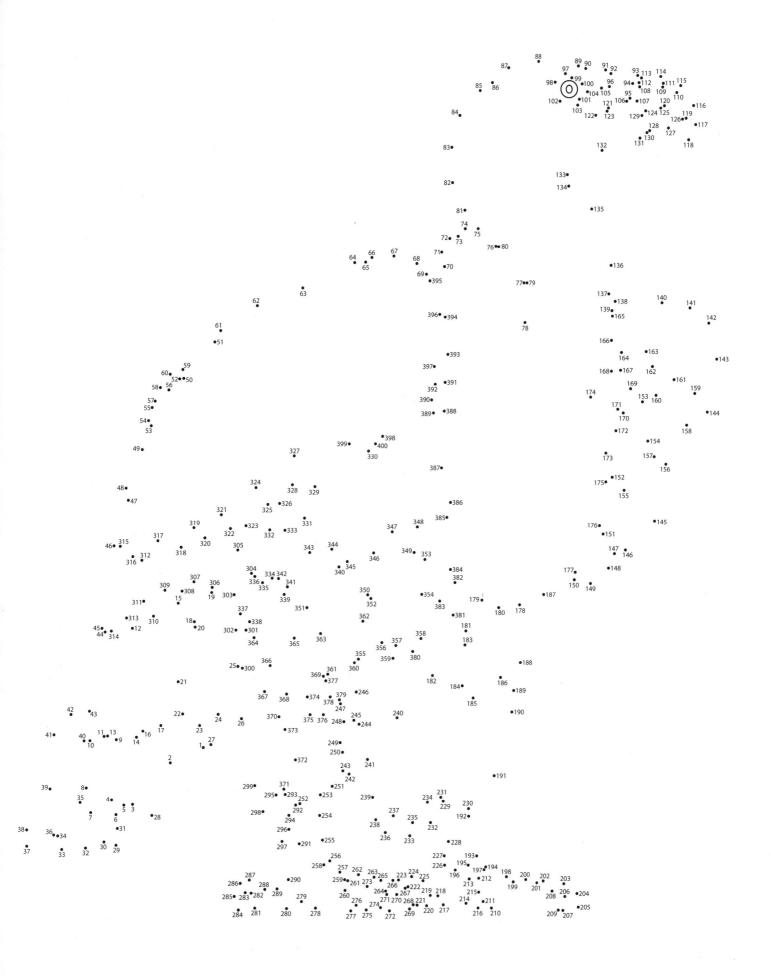

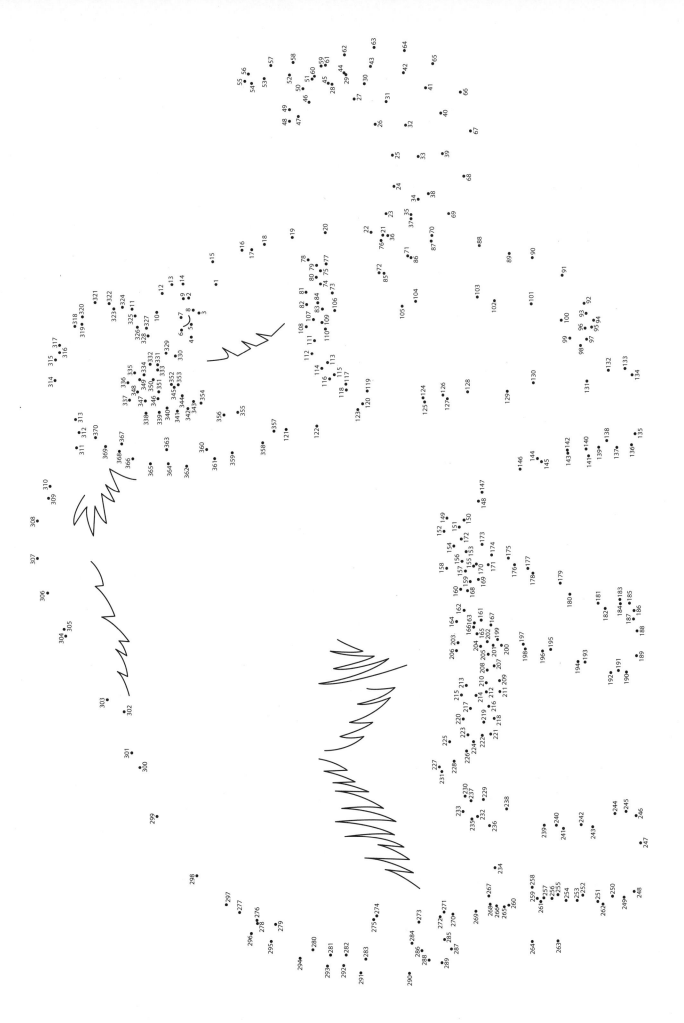

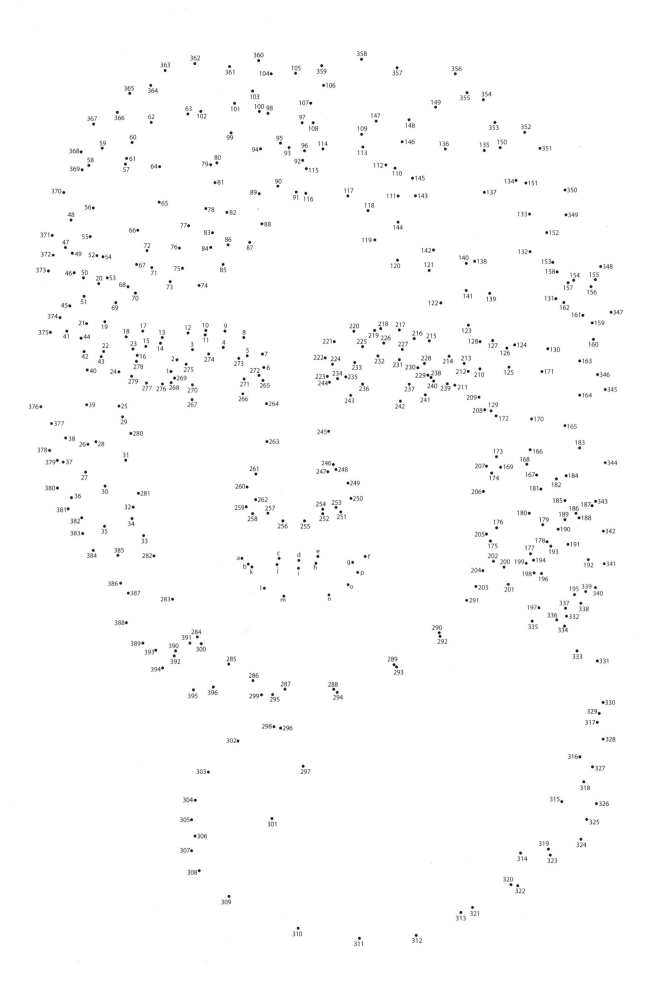

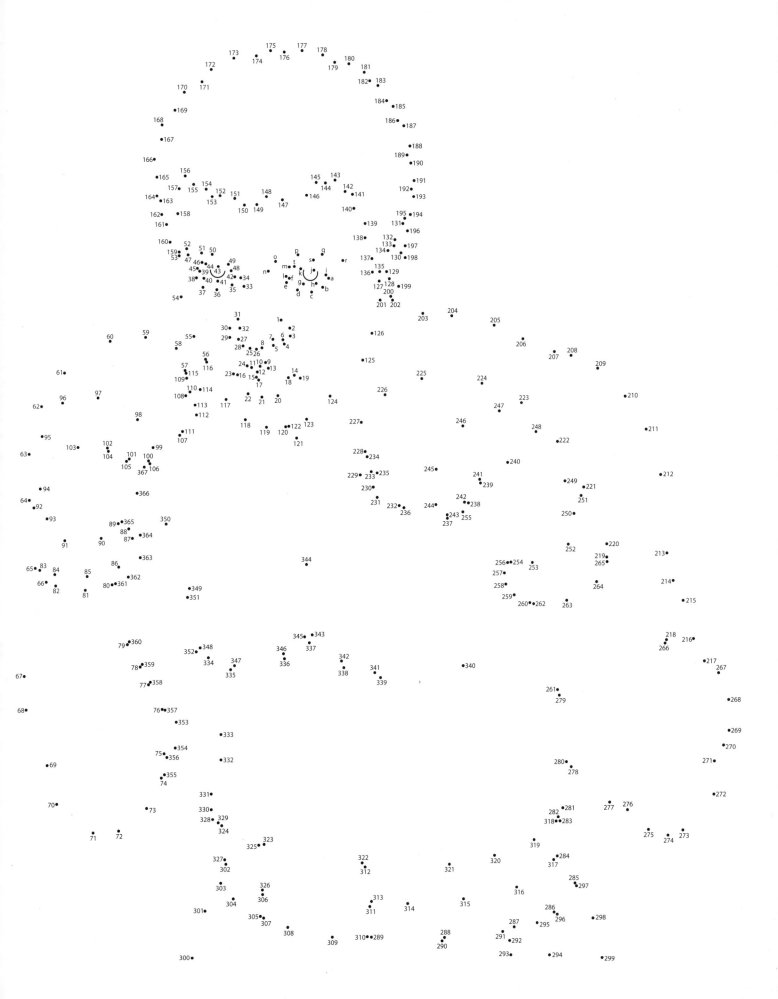

70

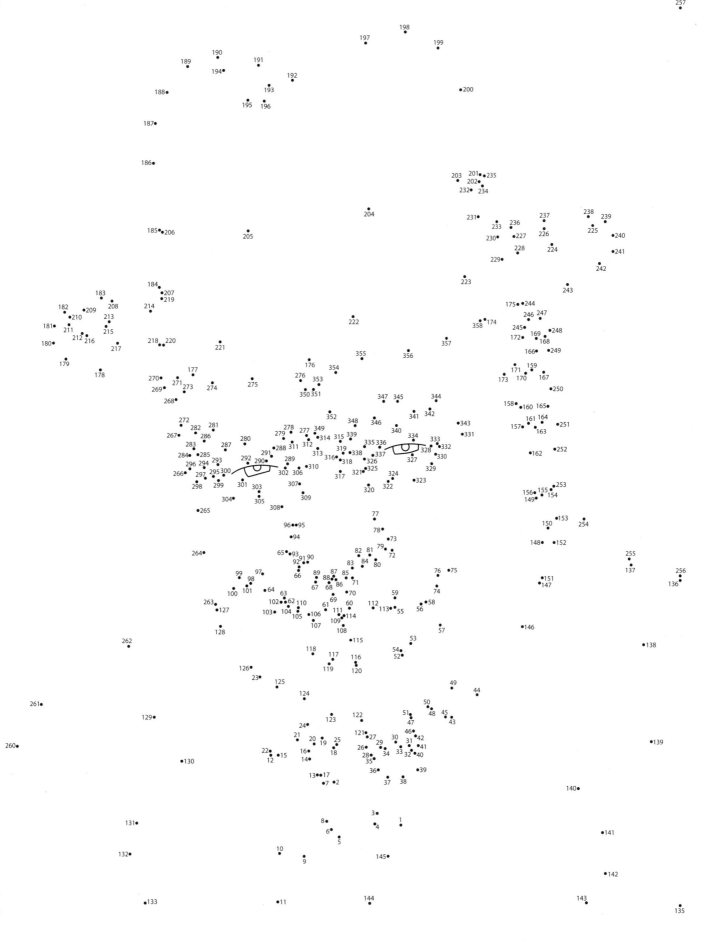

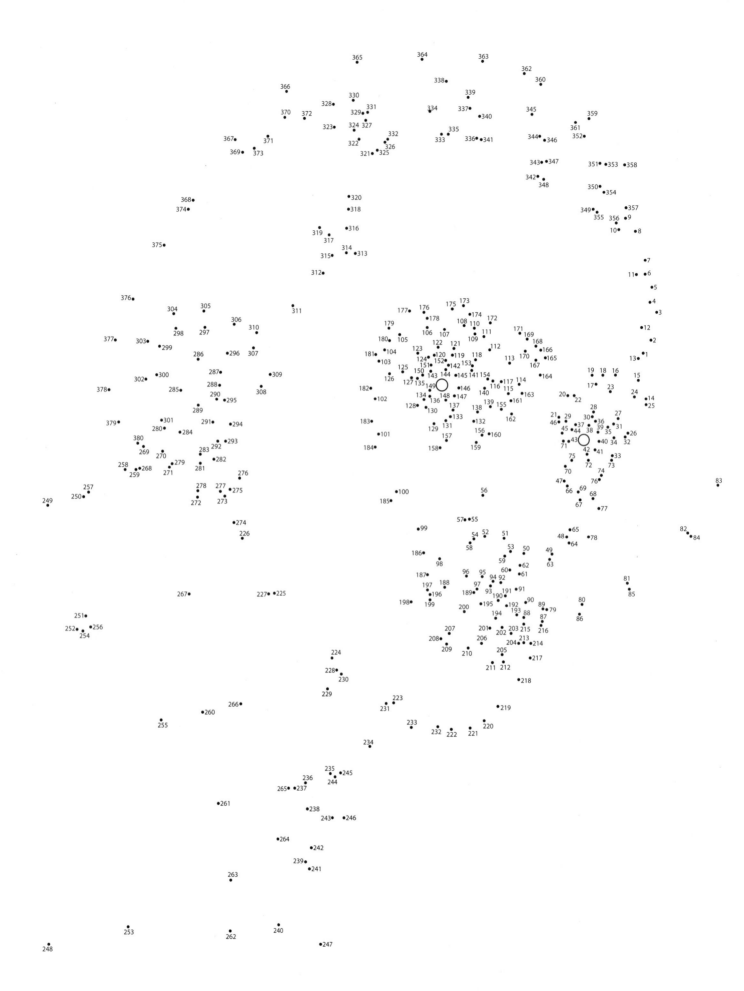

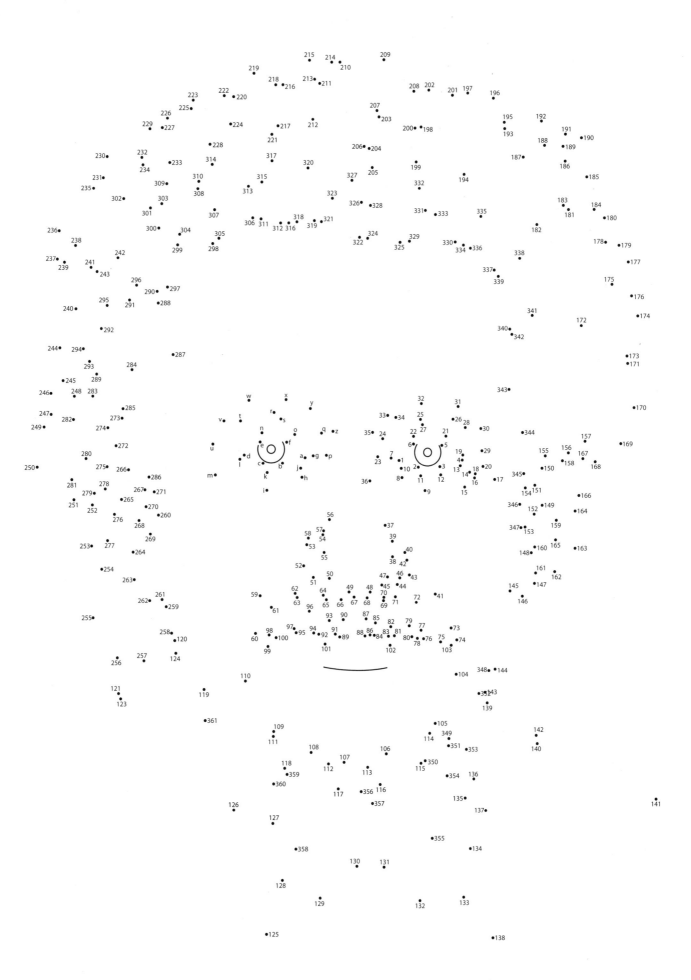

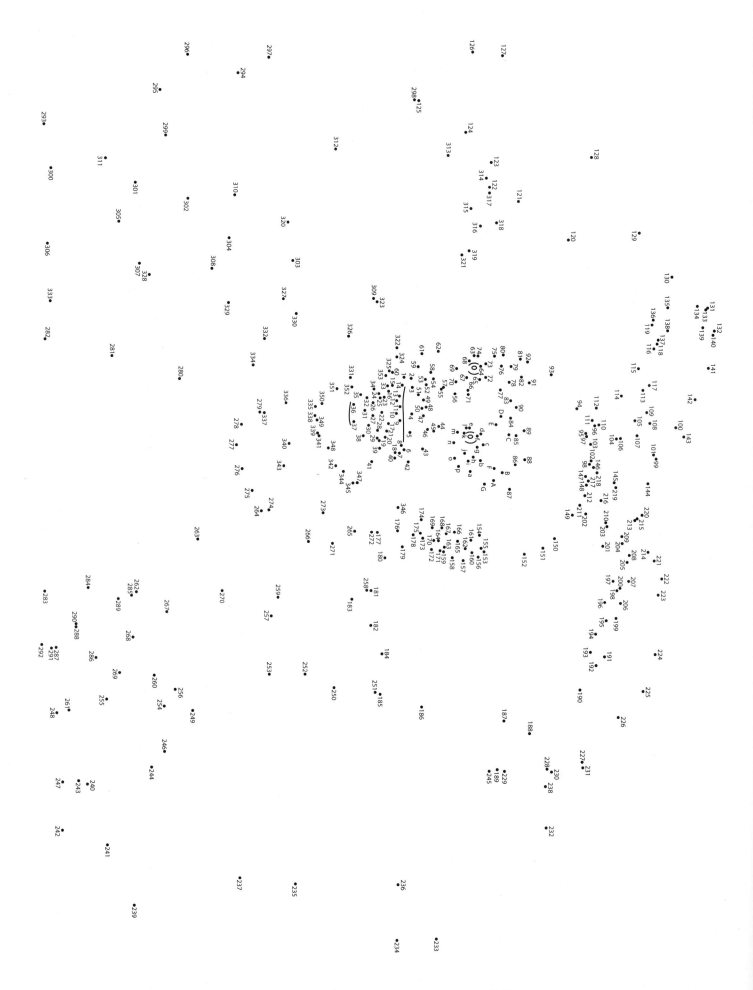

74

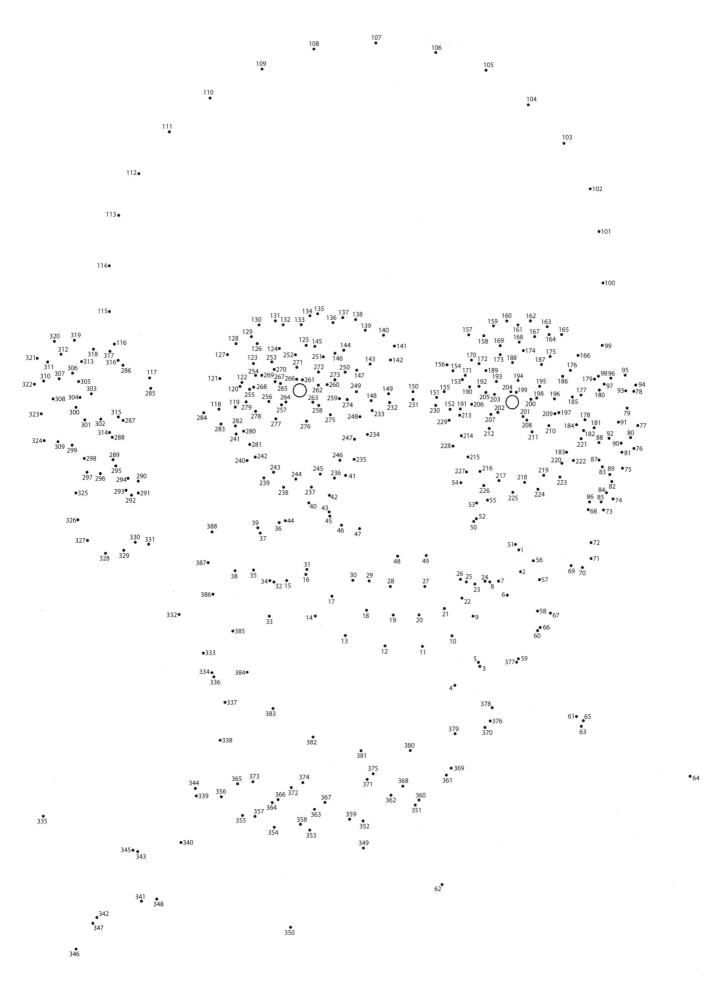

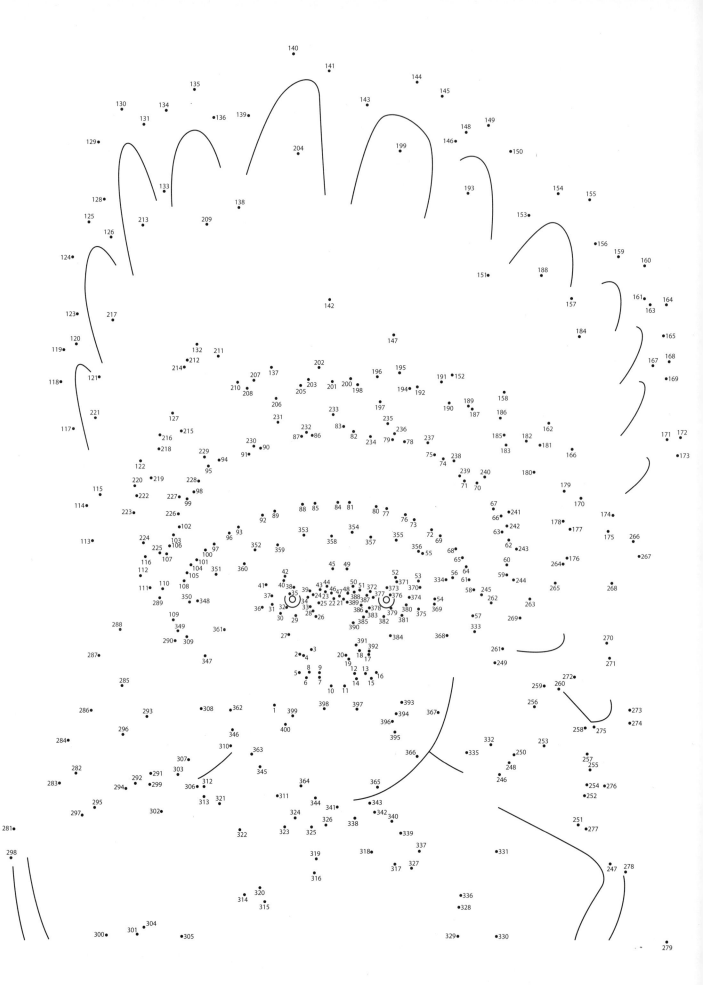

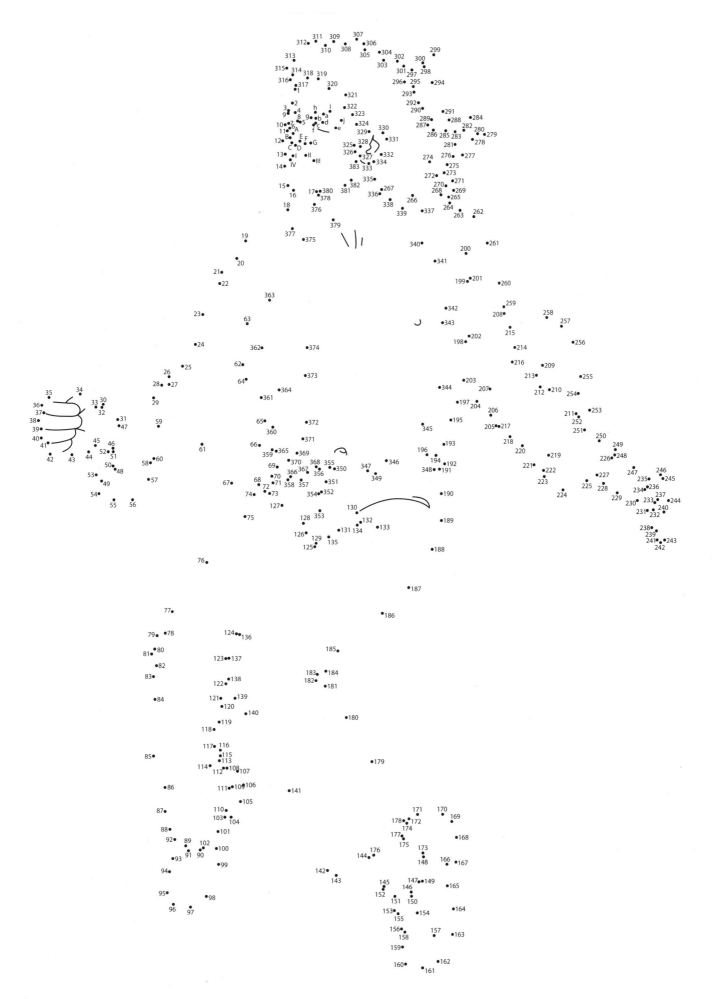

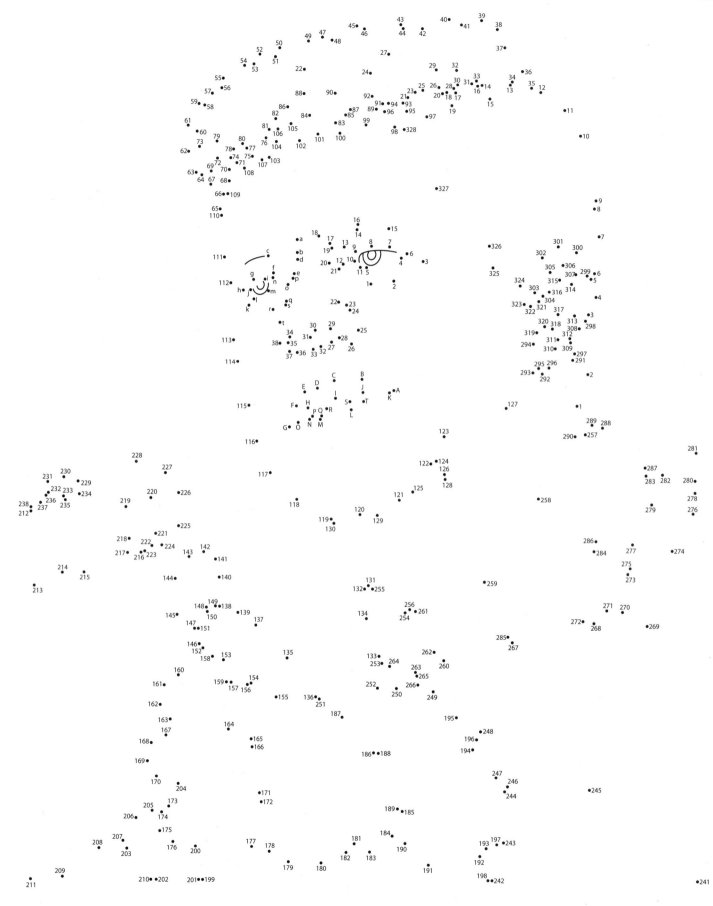

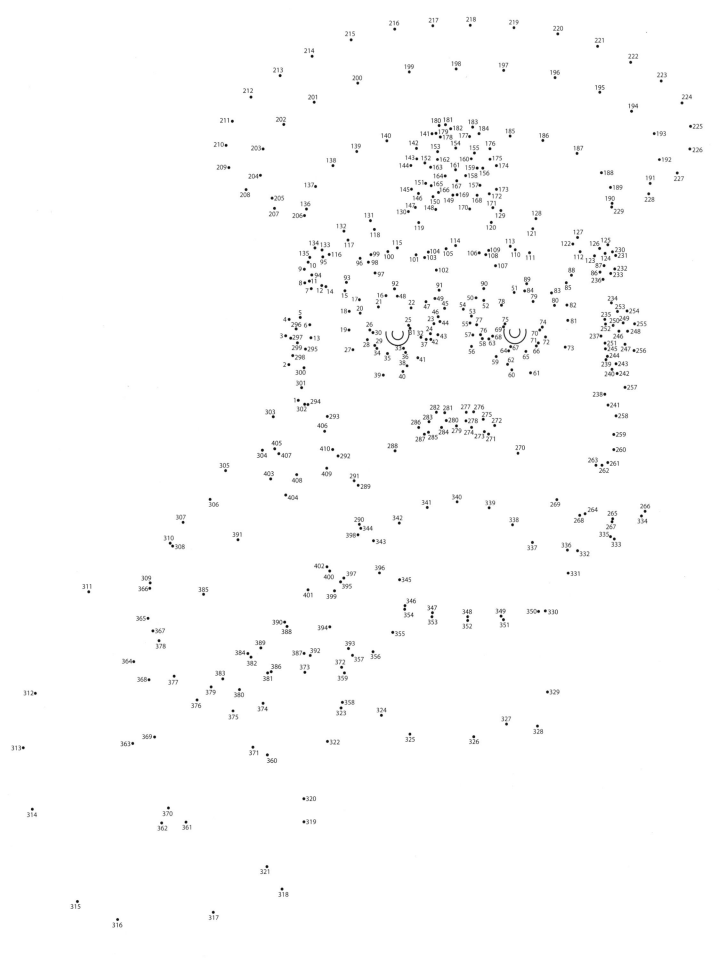

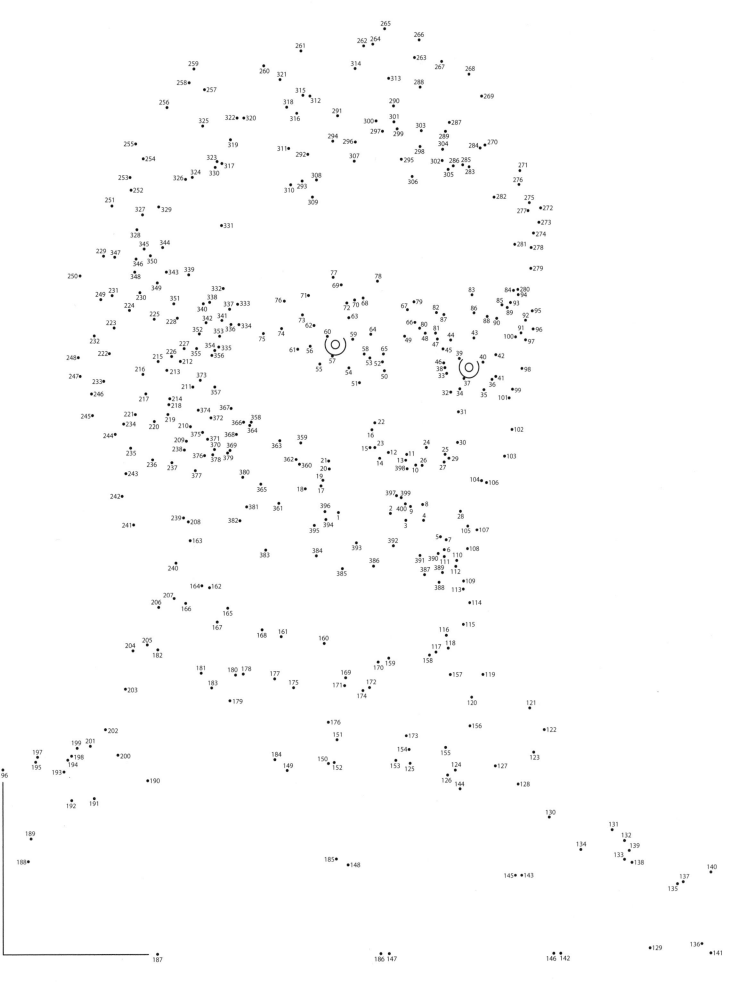

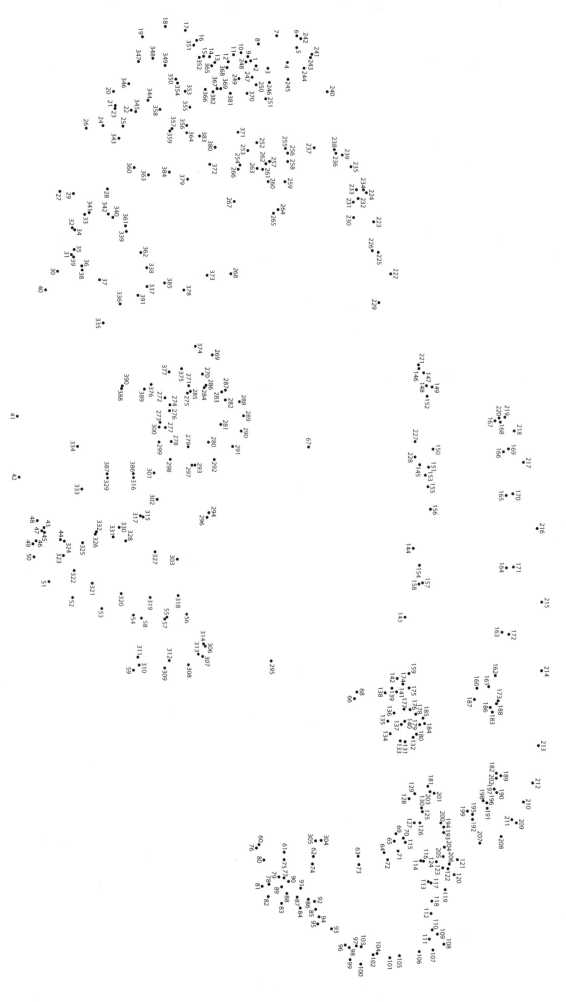

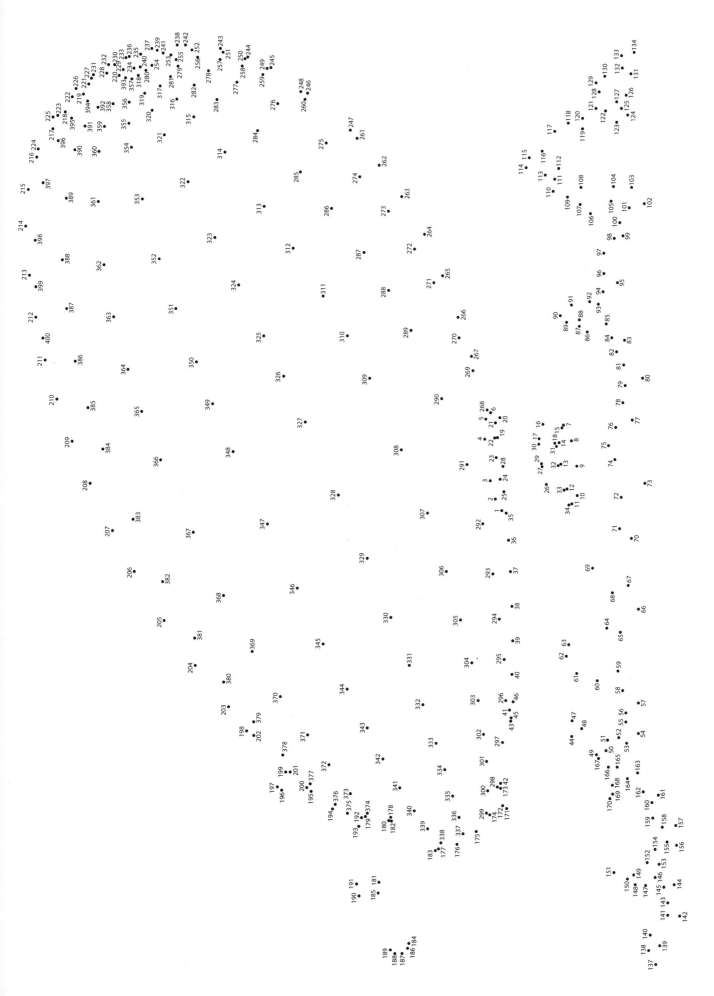

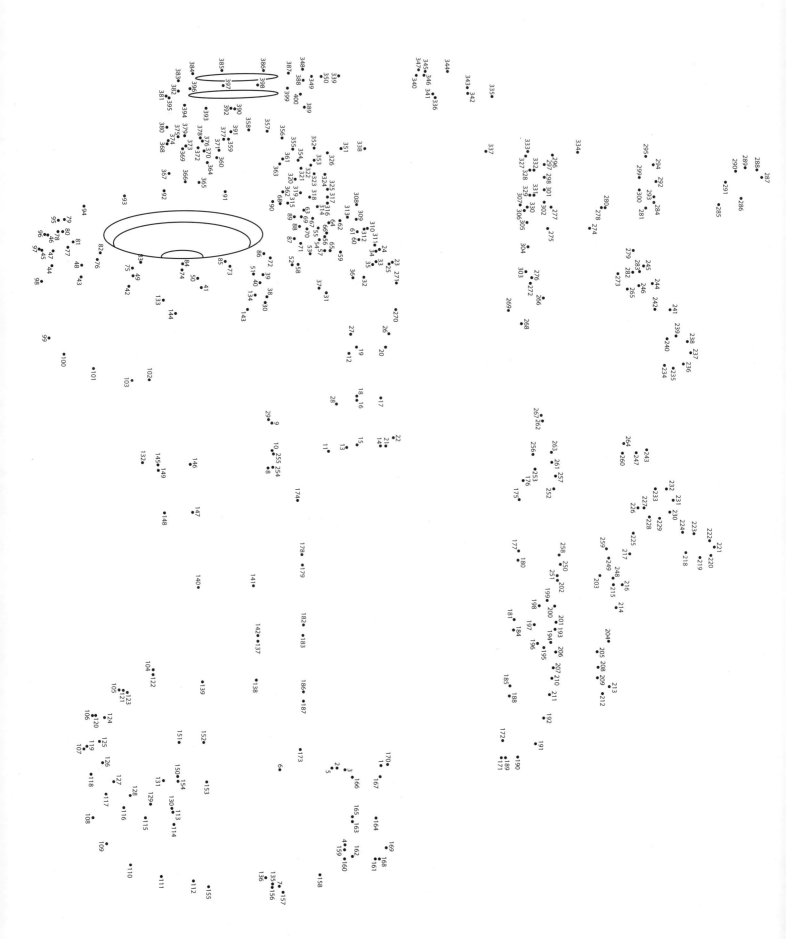

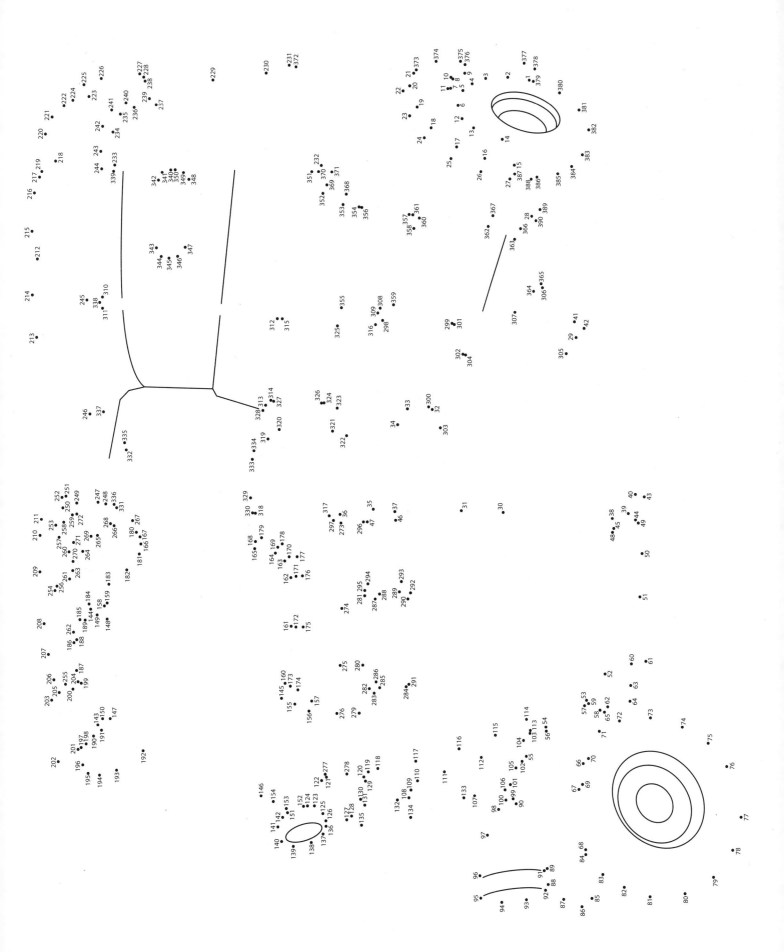

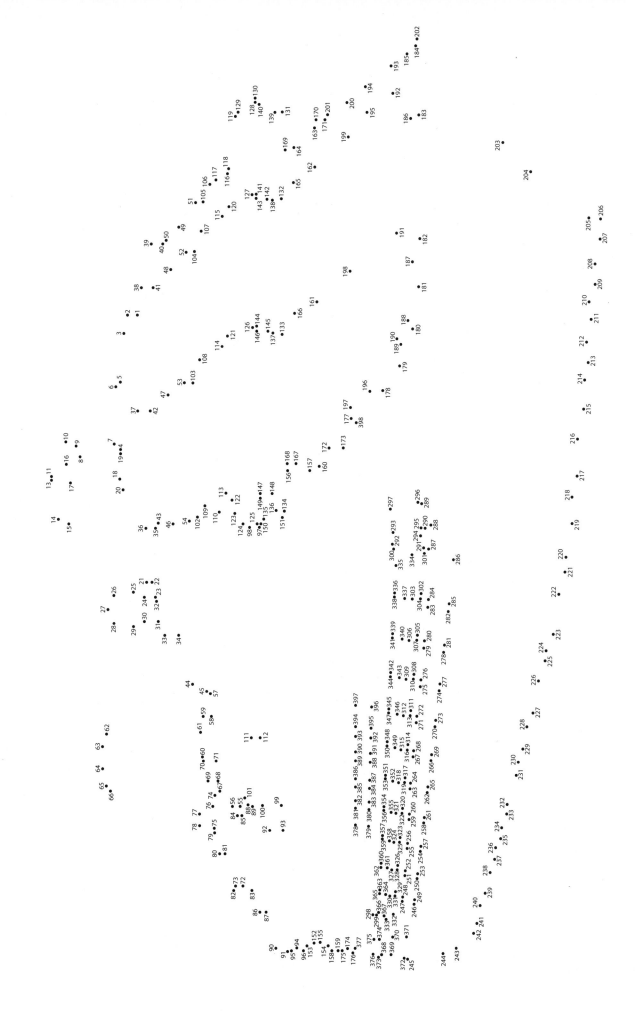

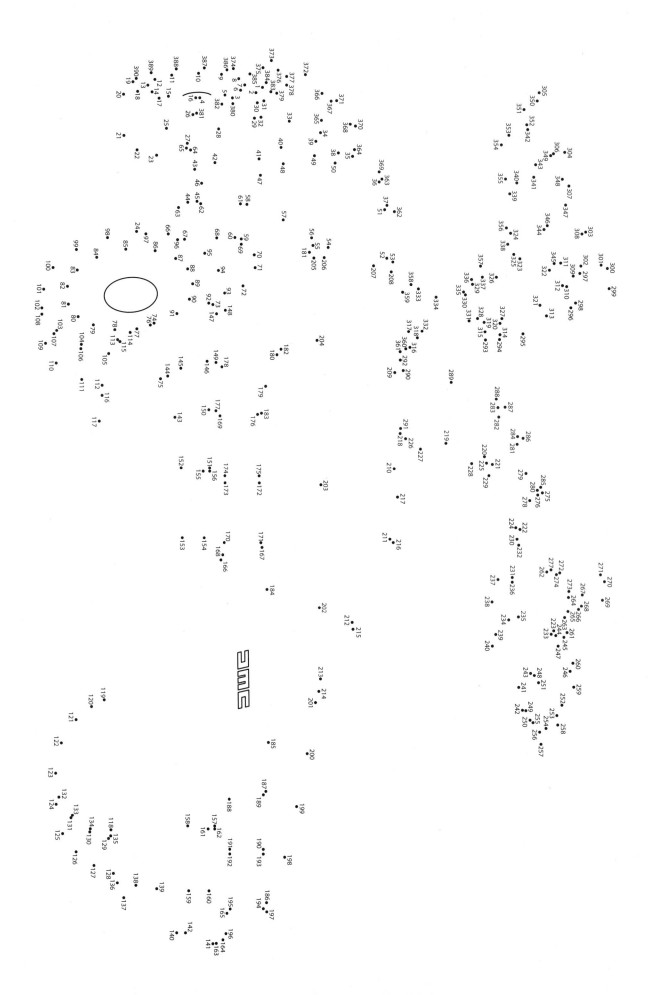

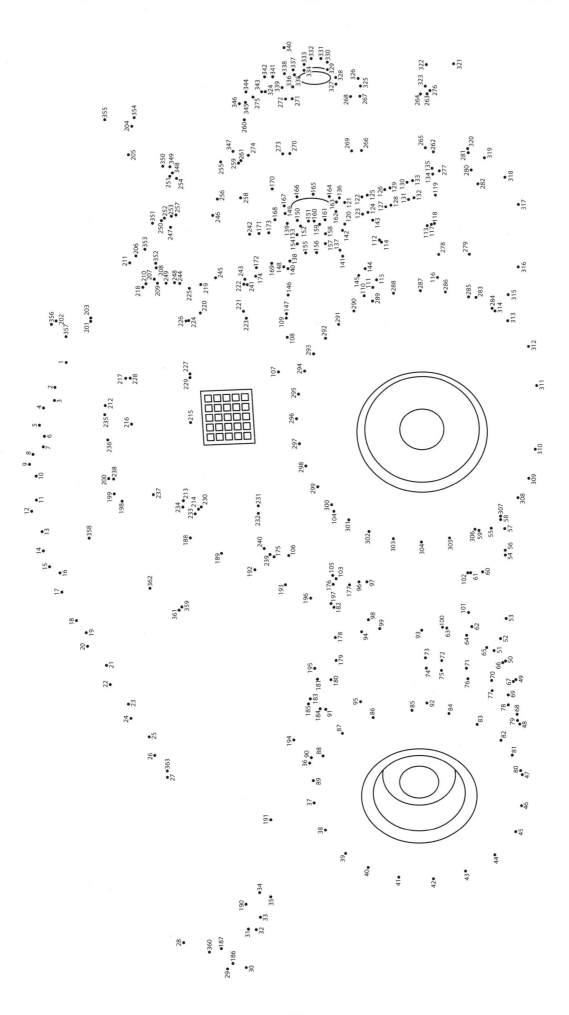

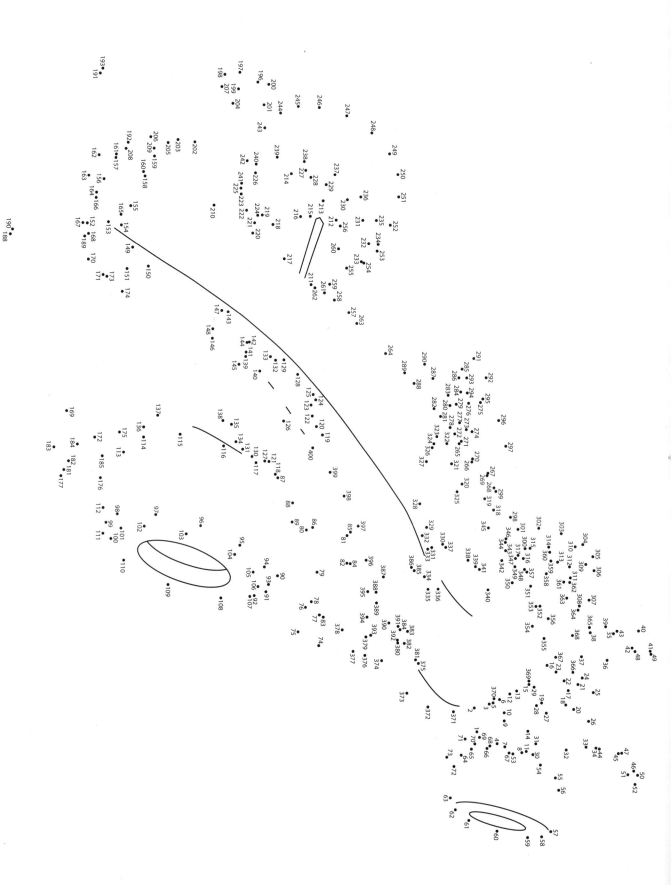

93

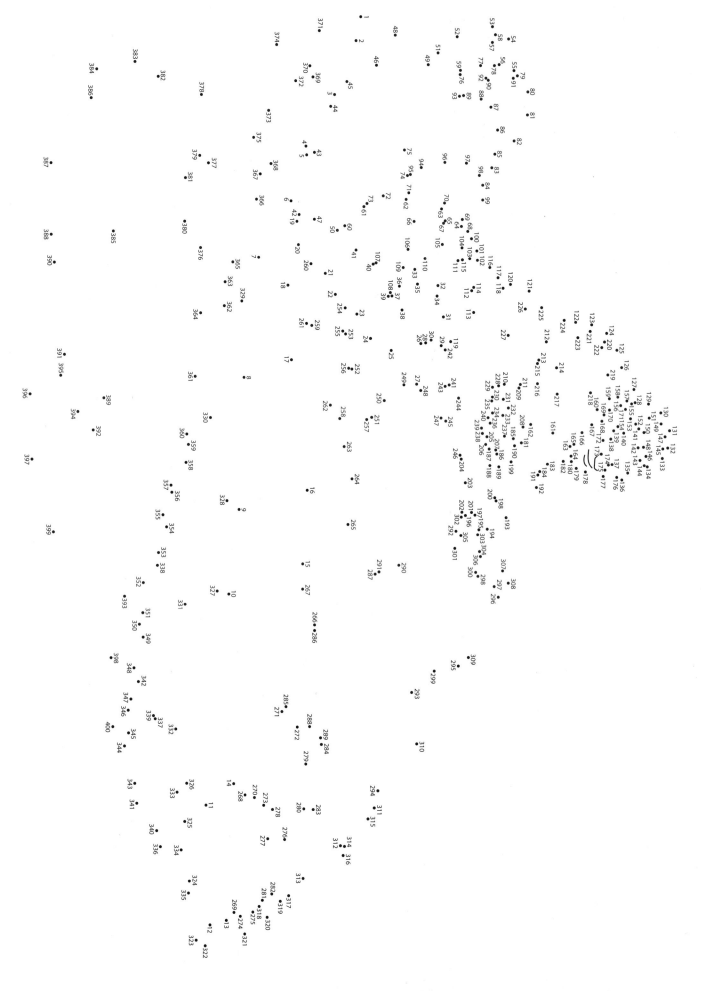

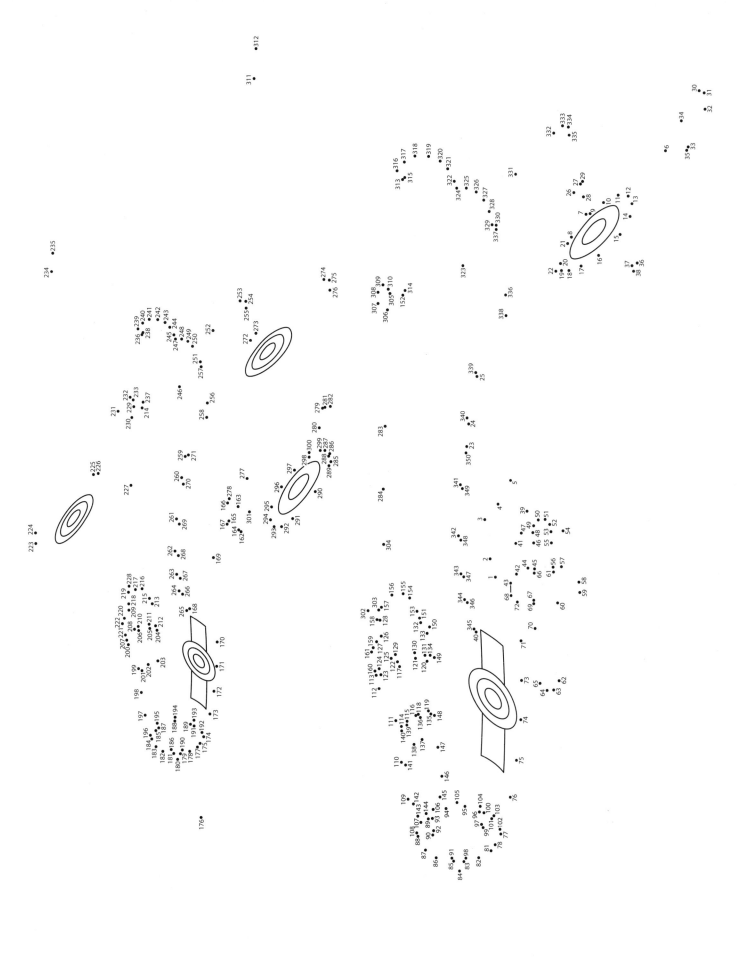

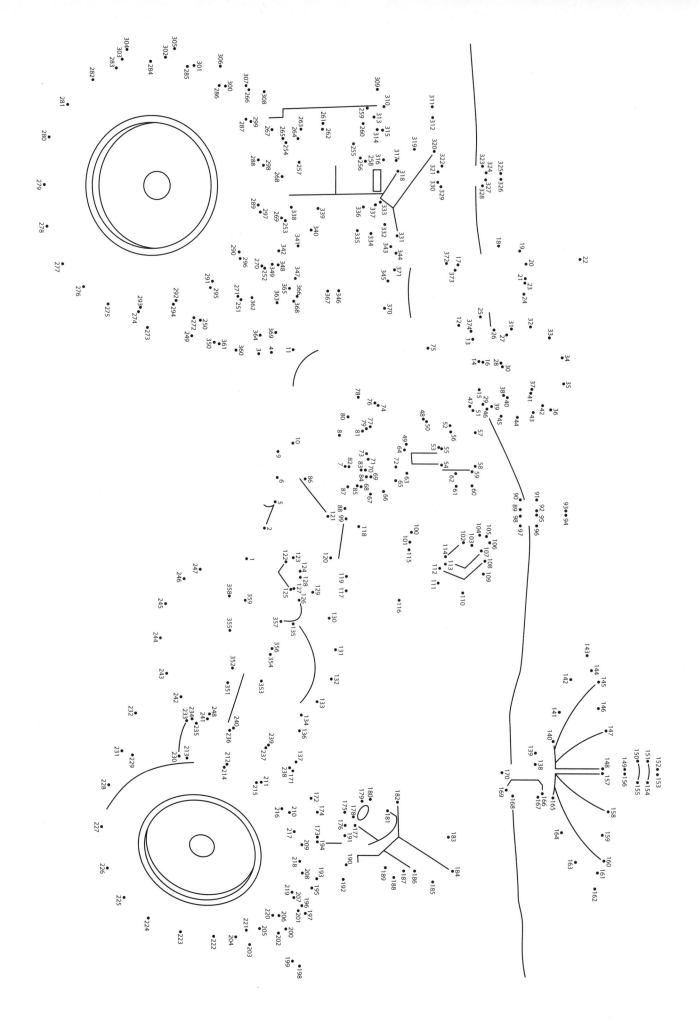

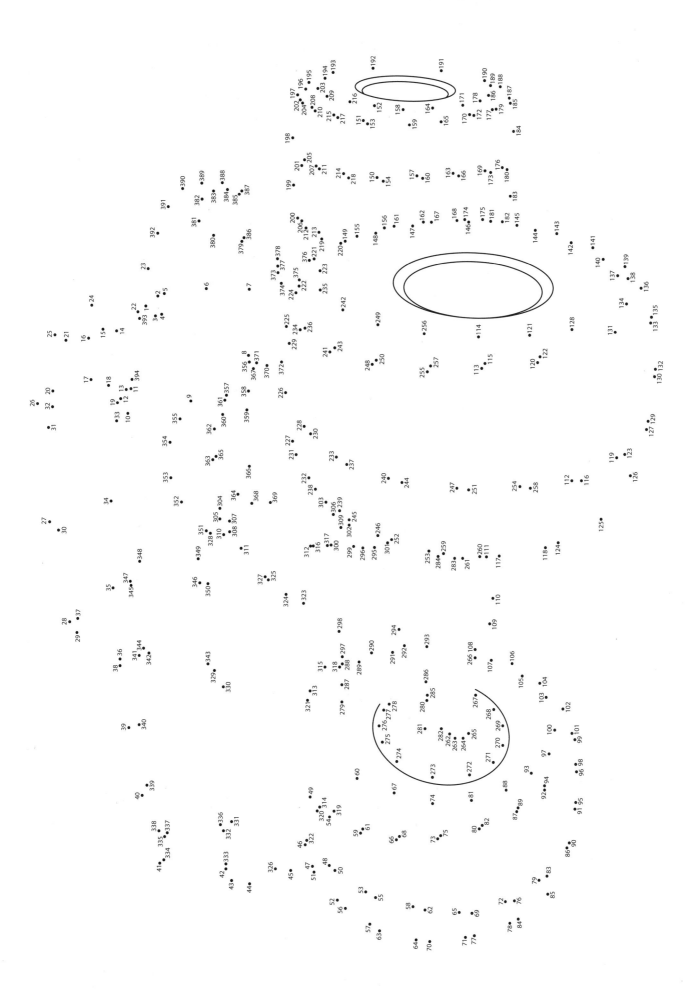

98

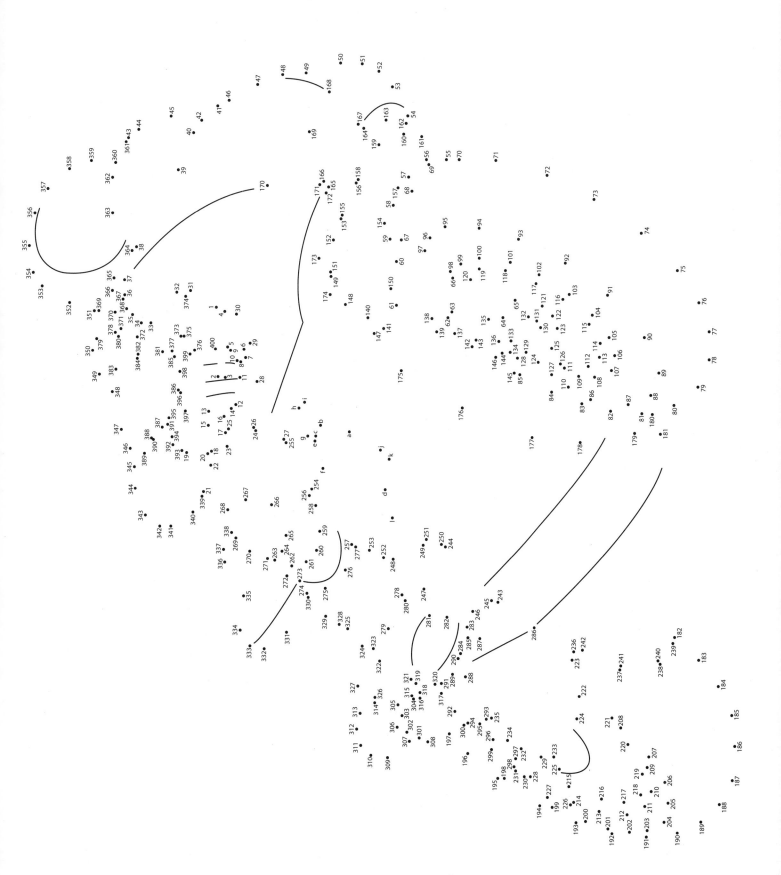

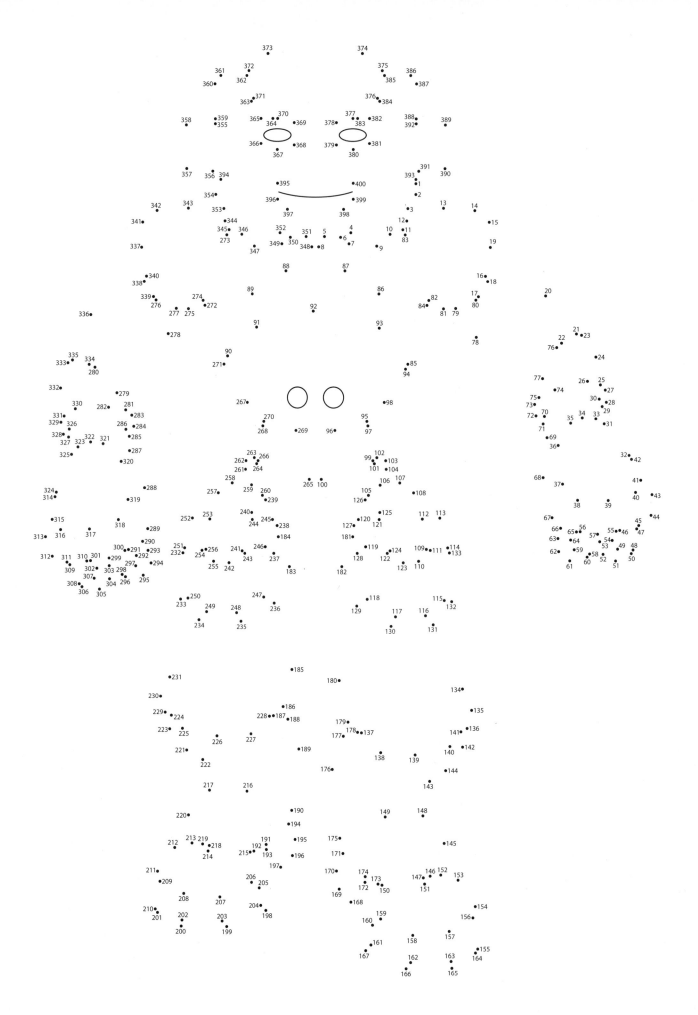

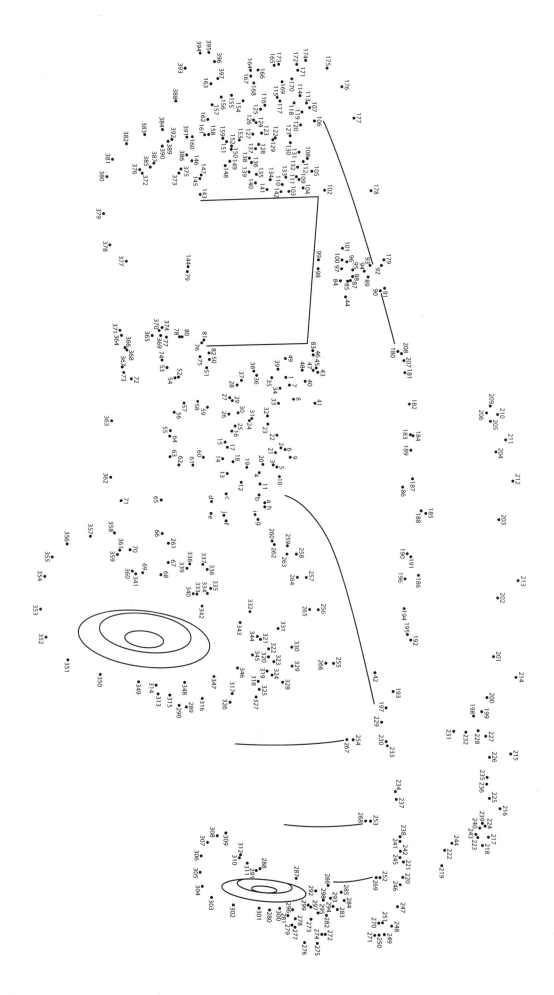

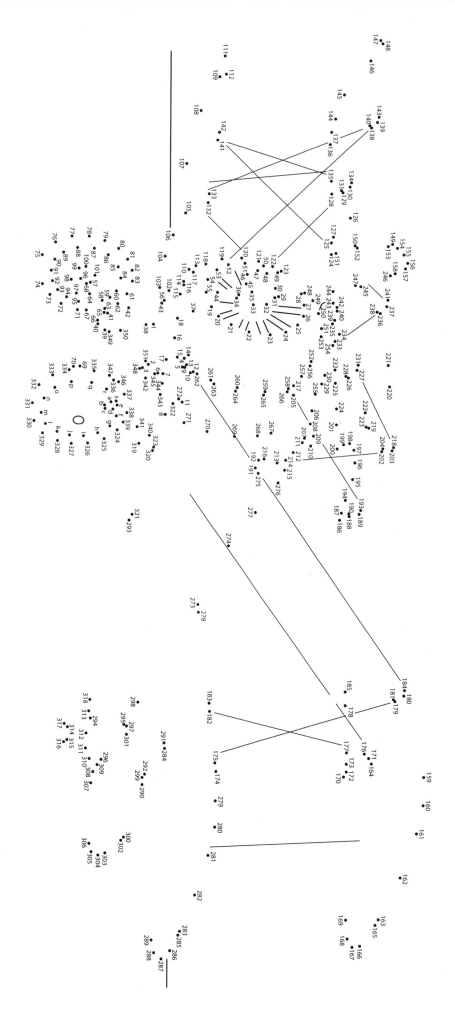

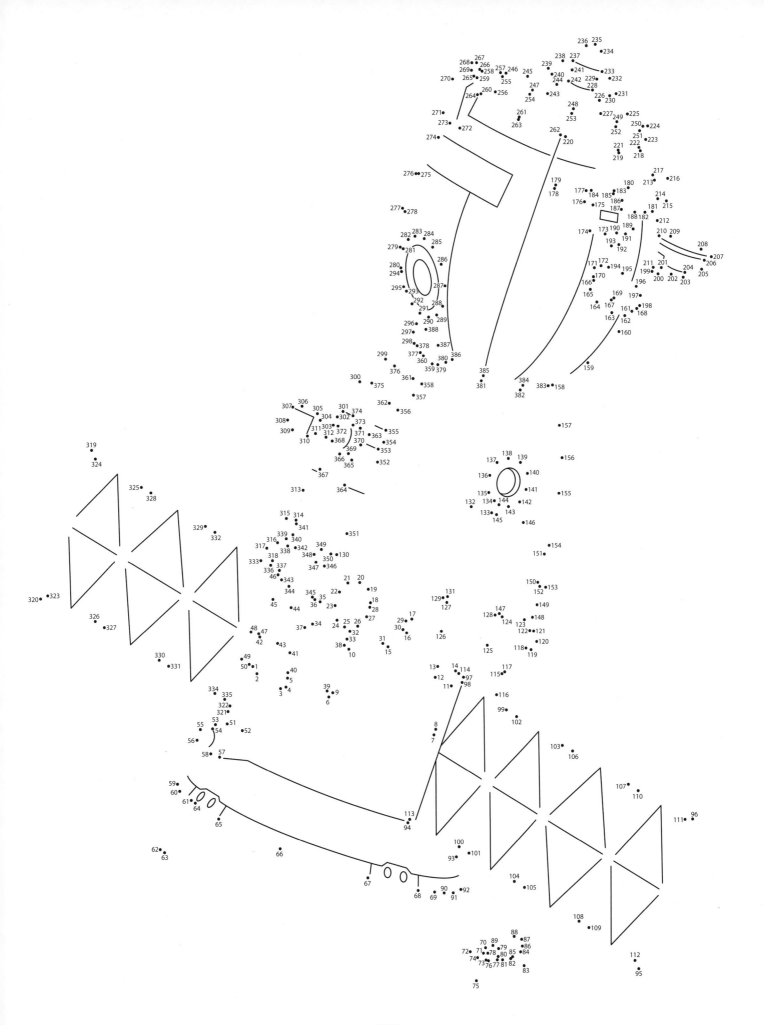

107

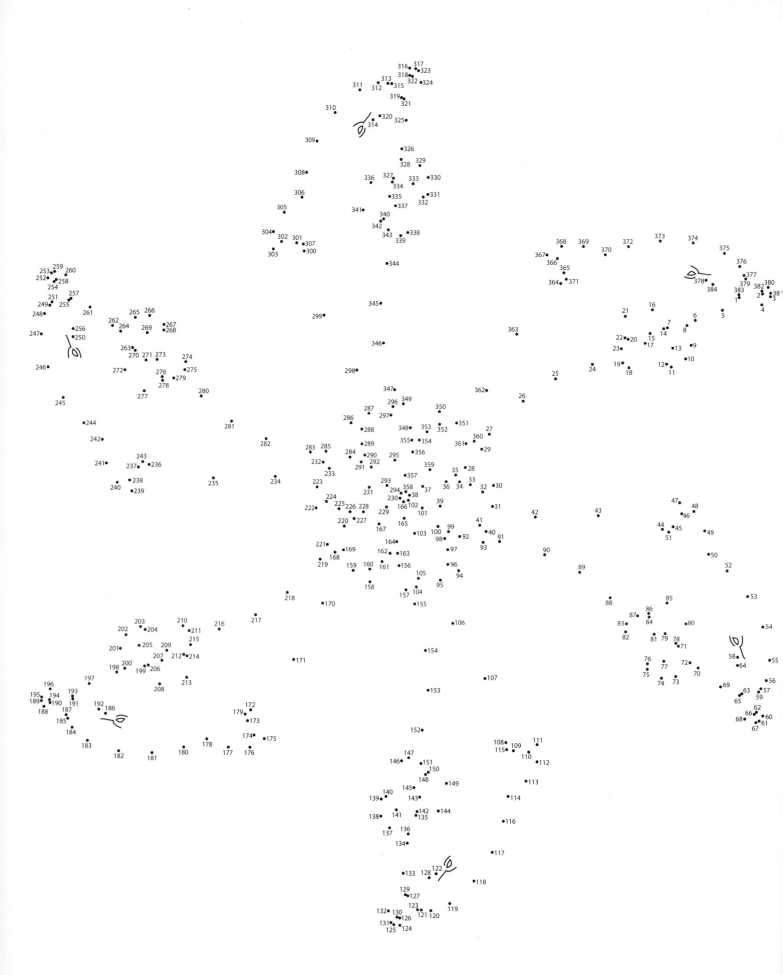

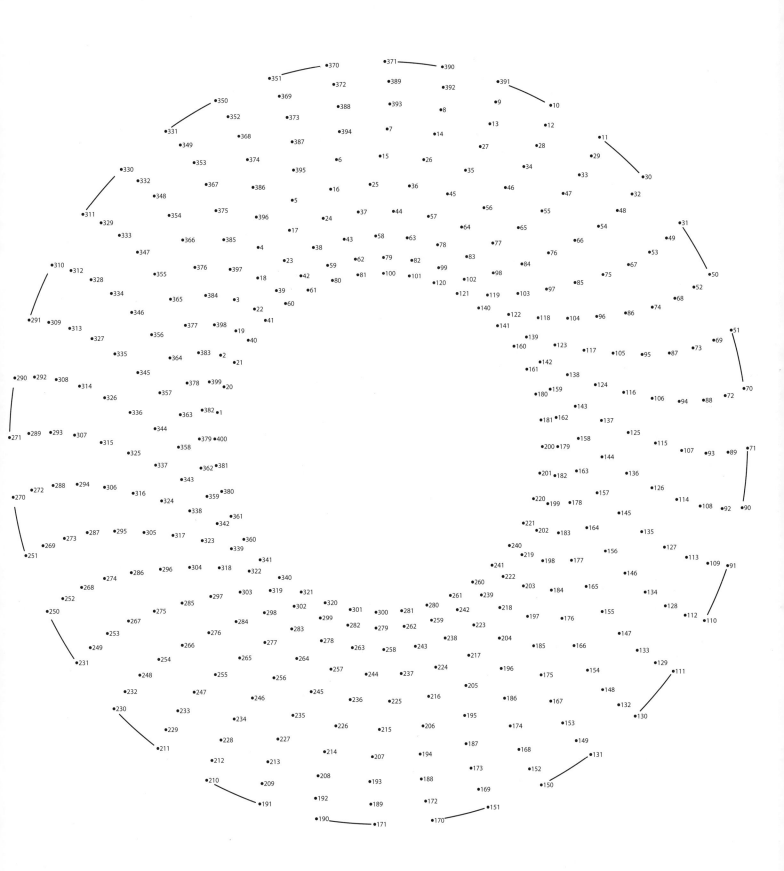

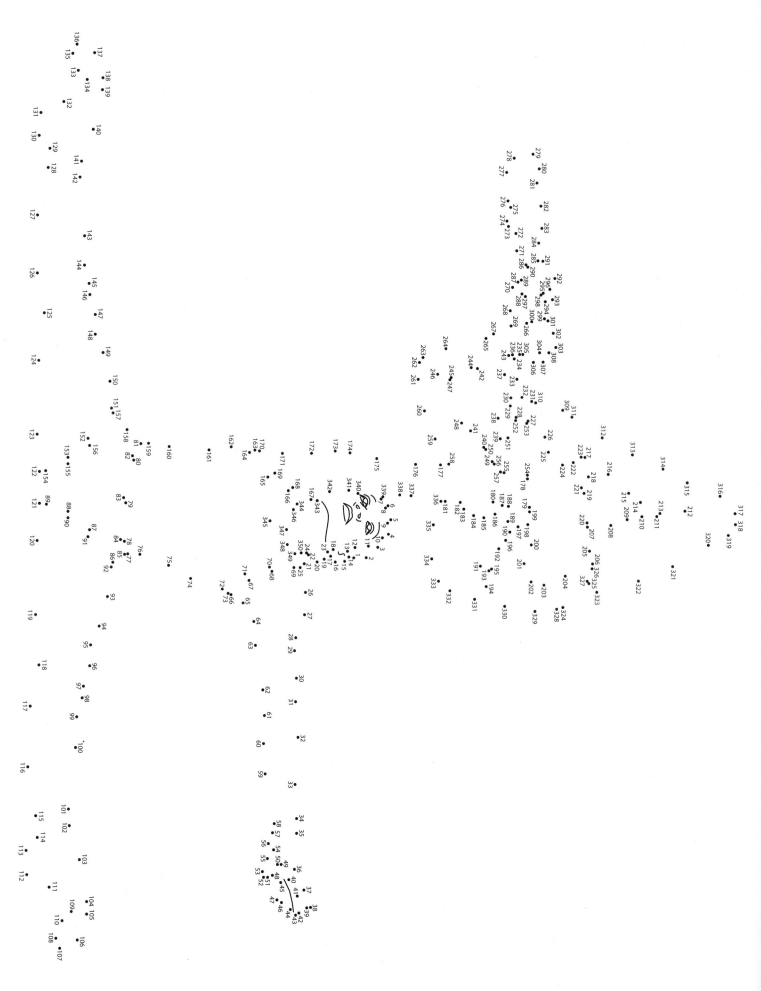

110

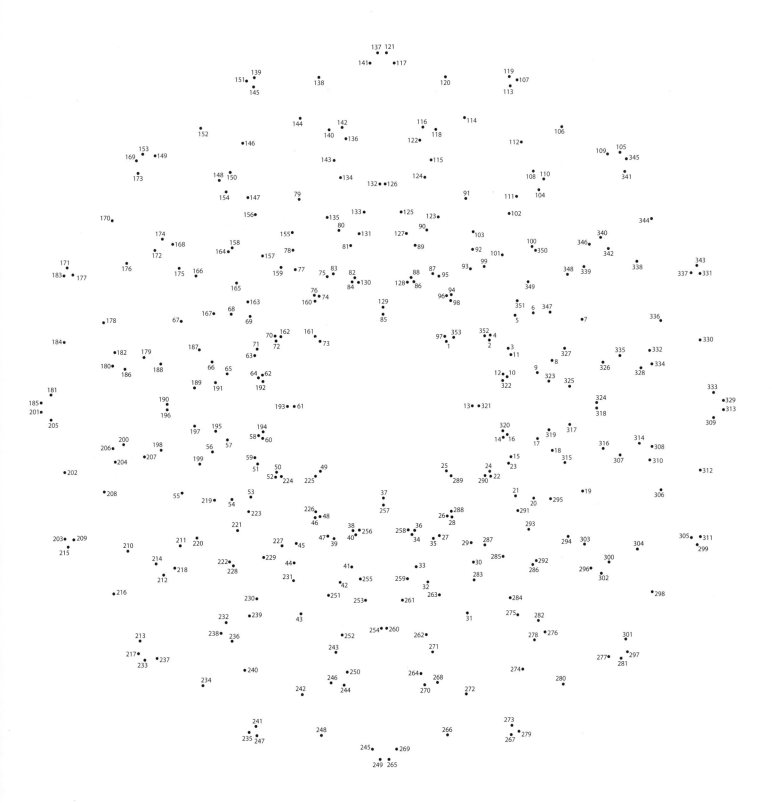

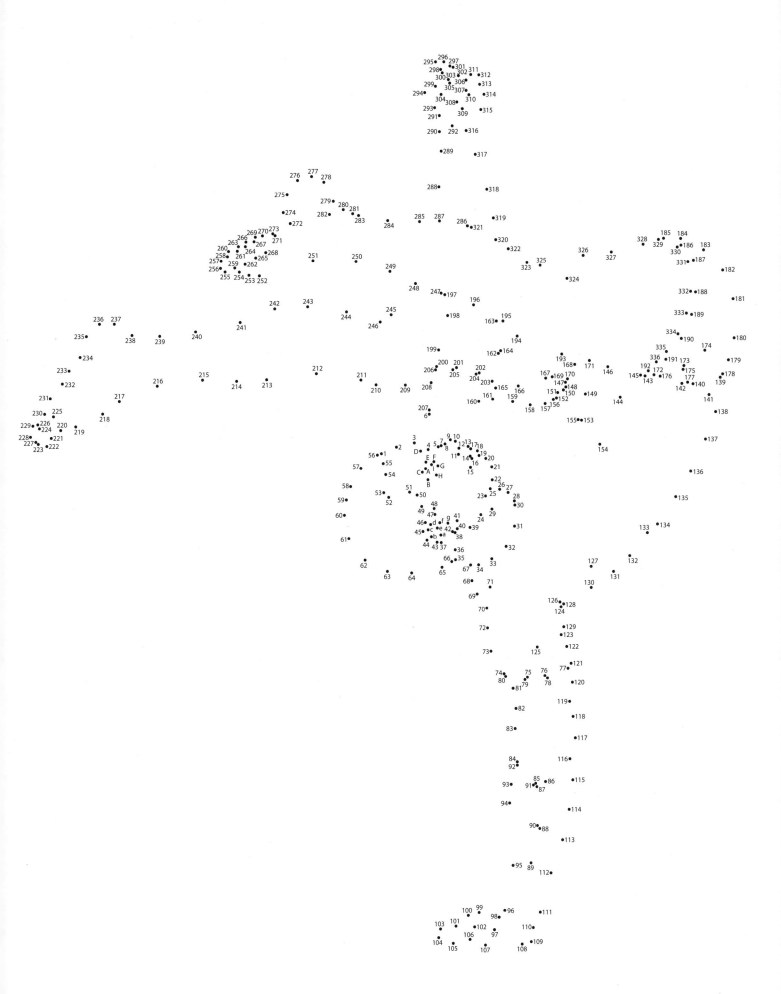

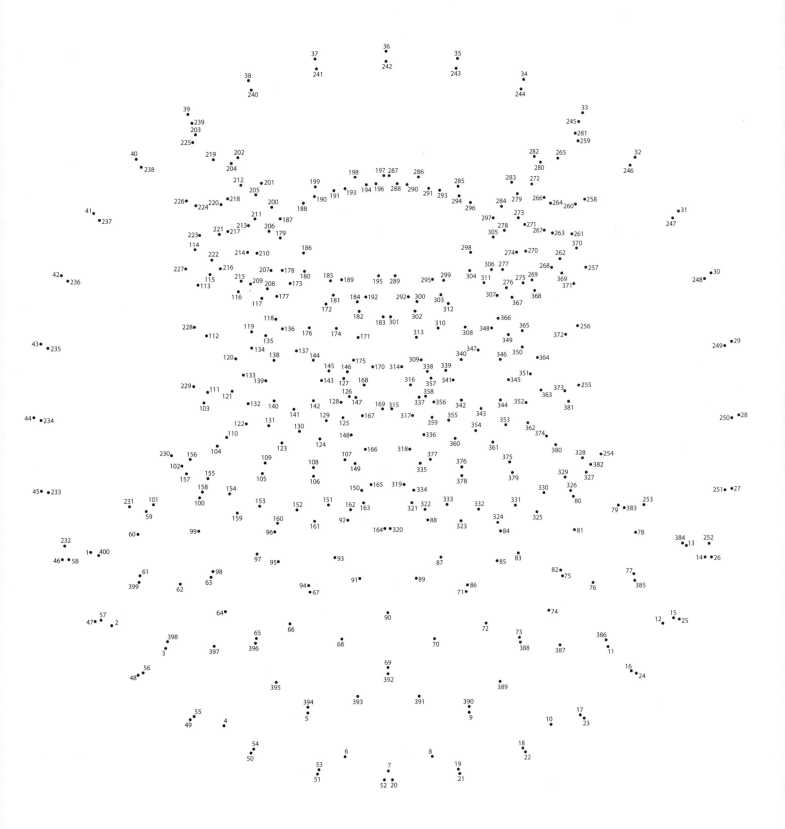

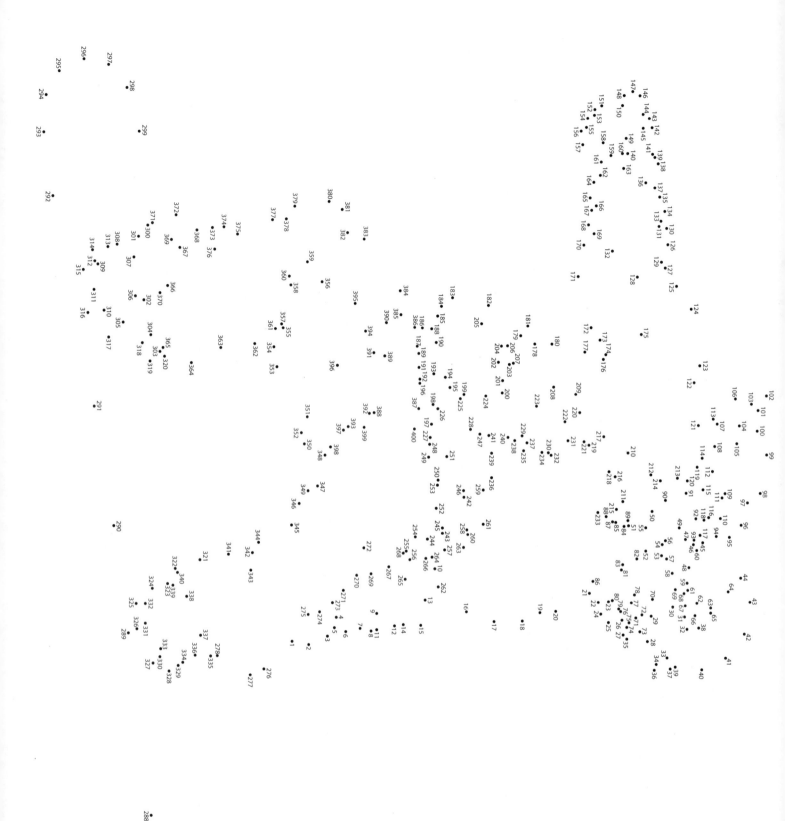

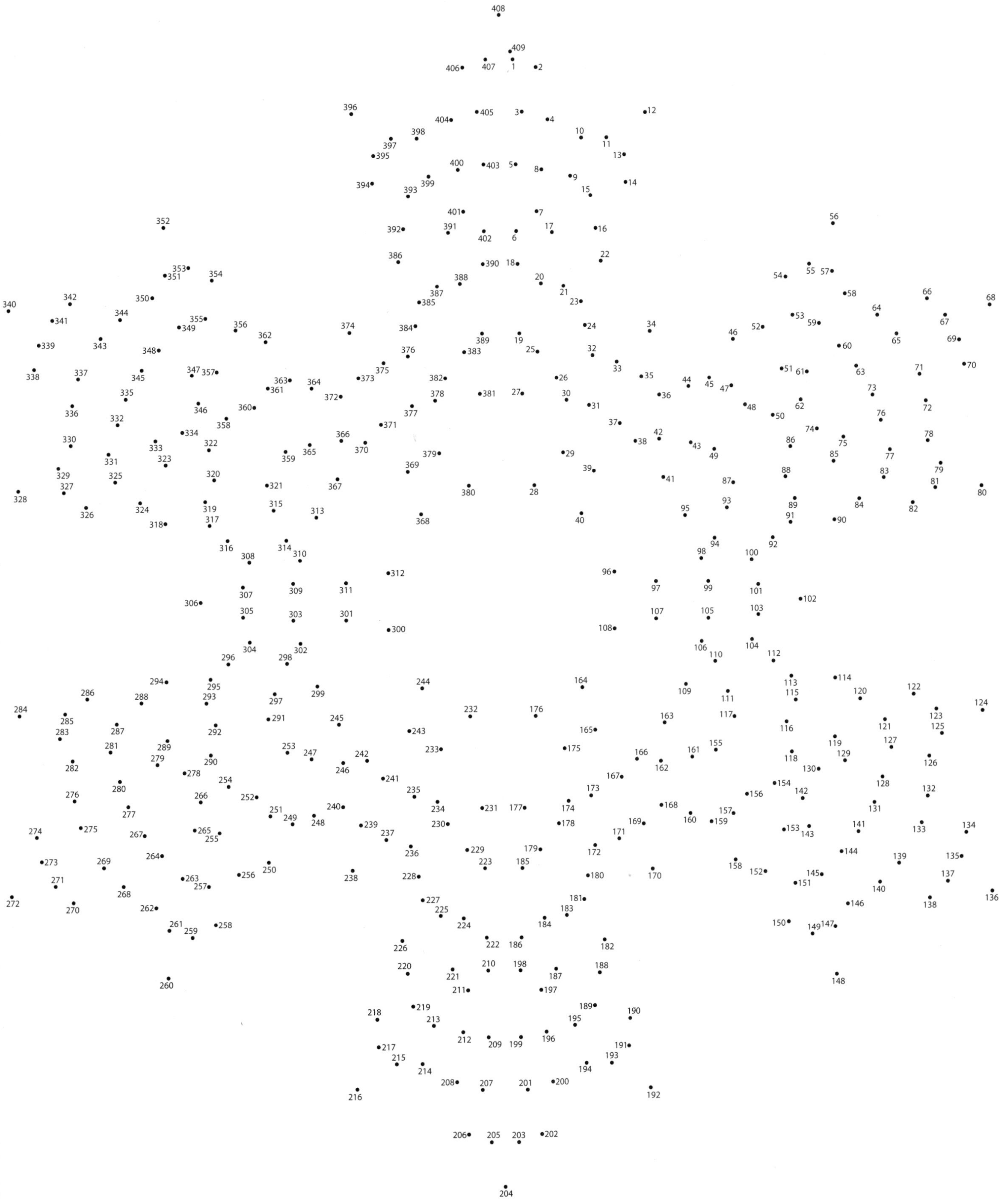

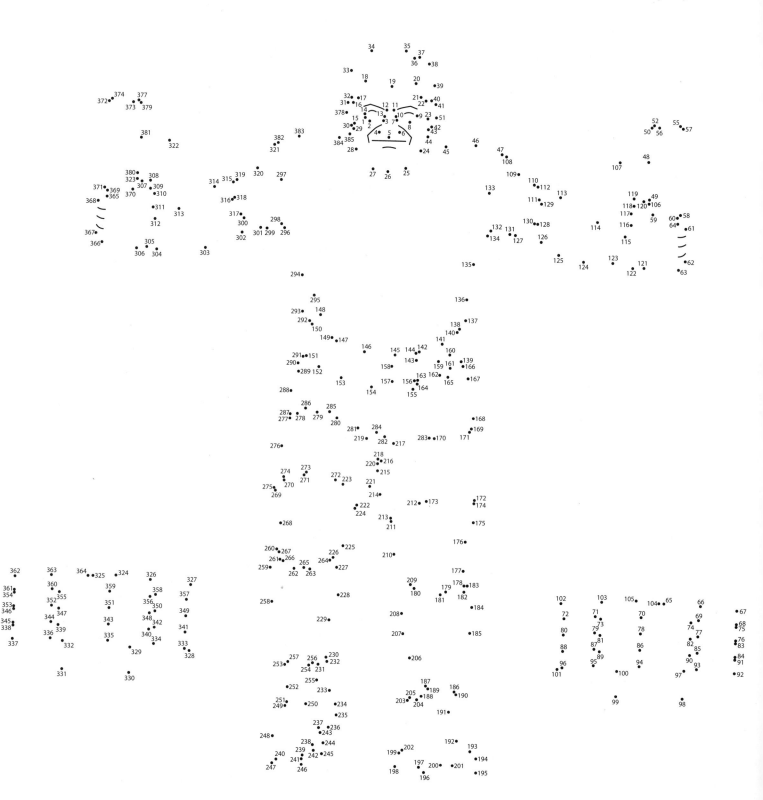

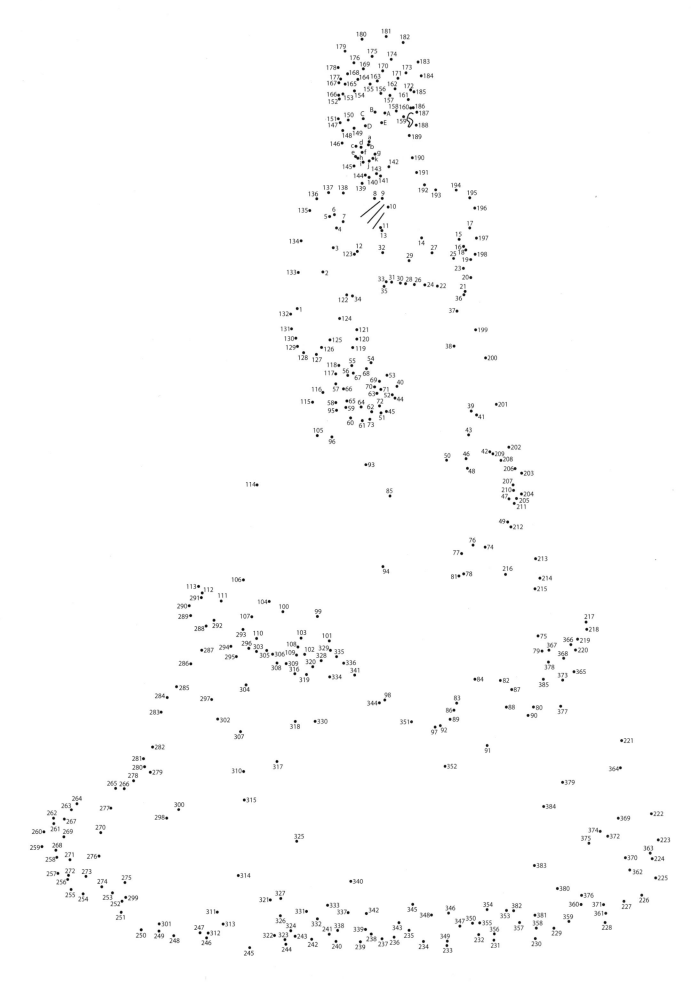

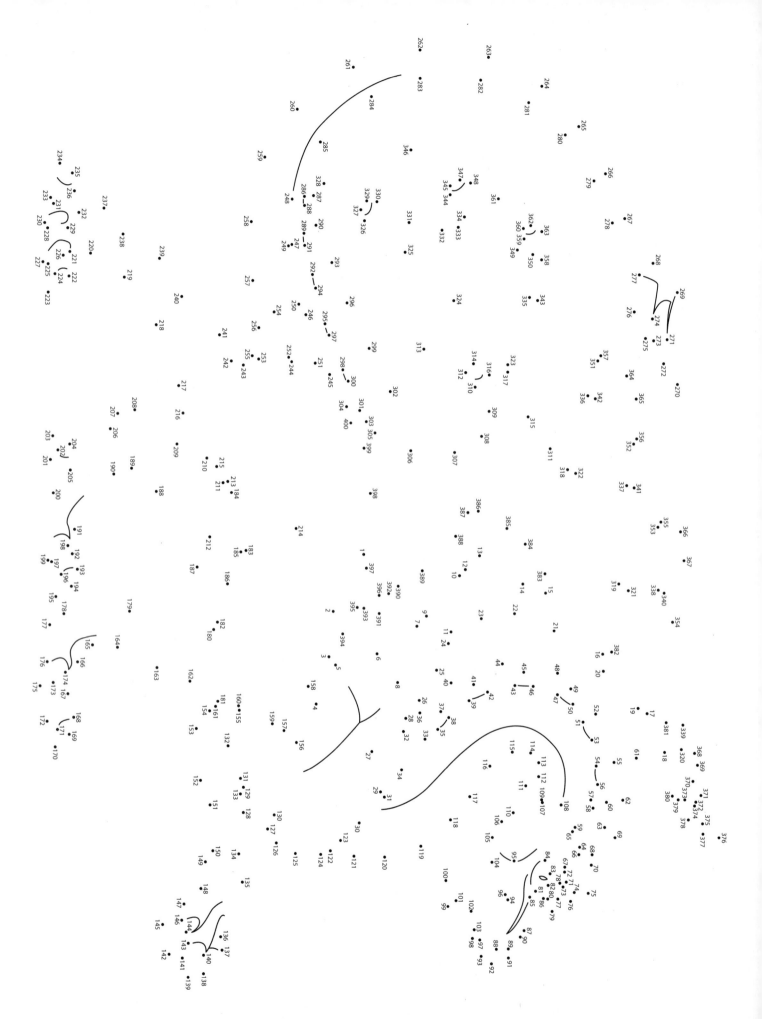

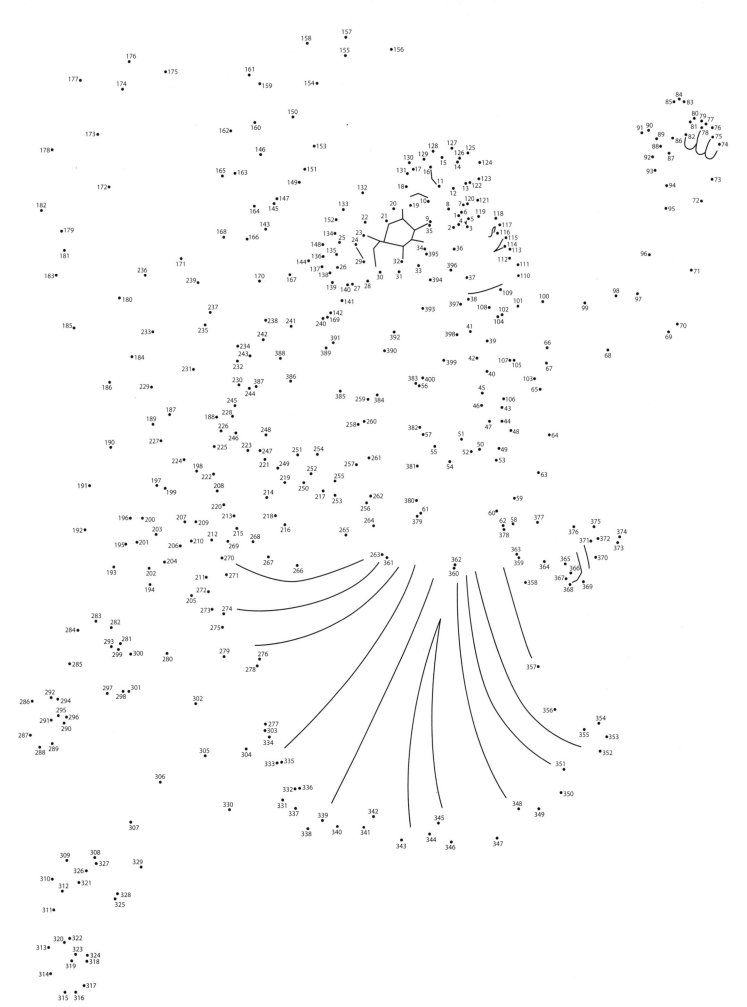

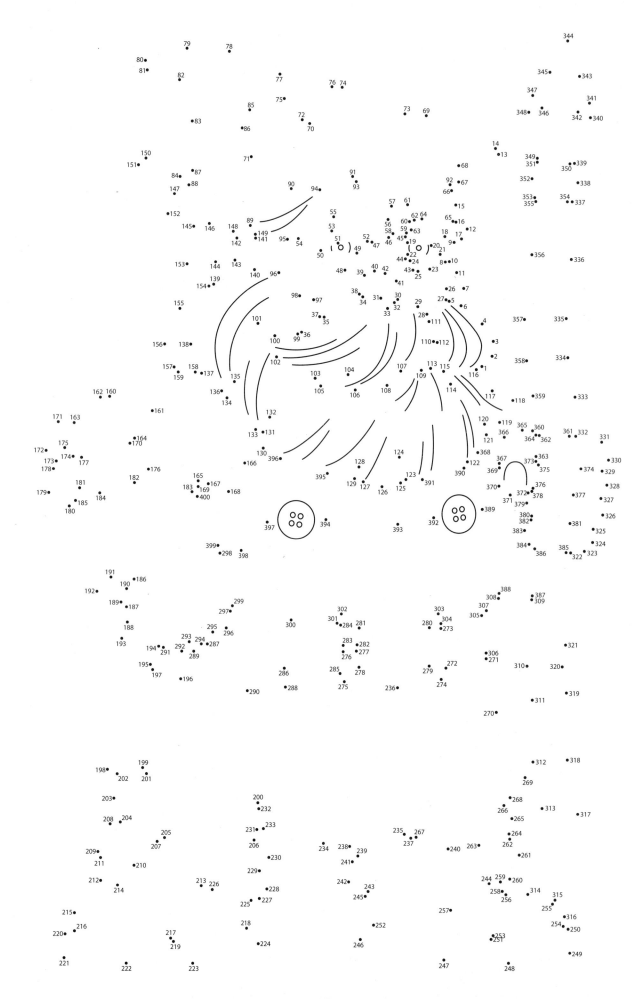

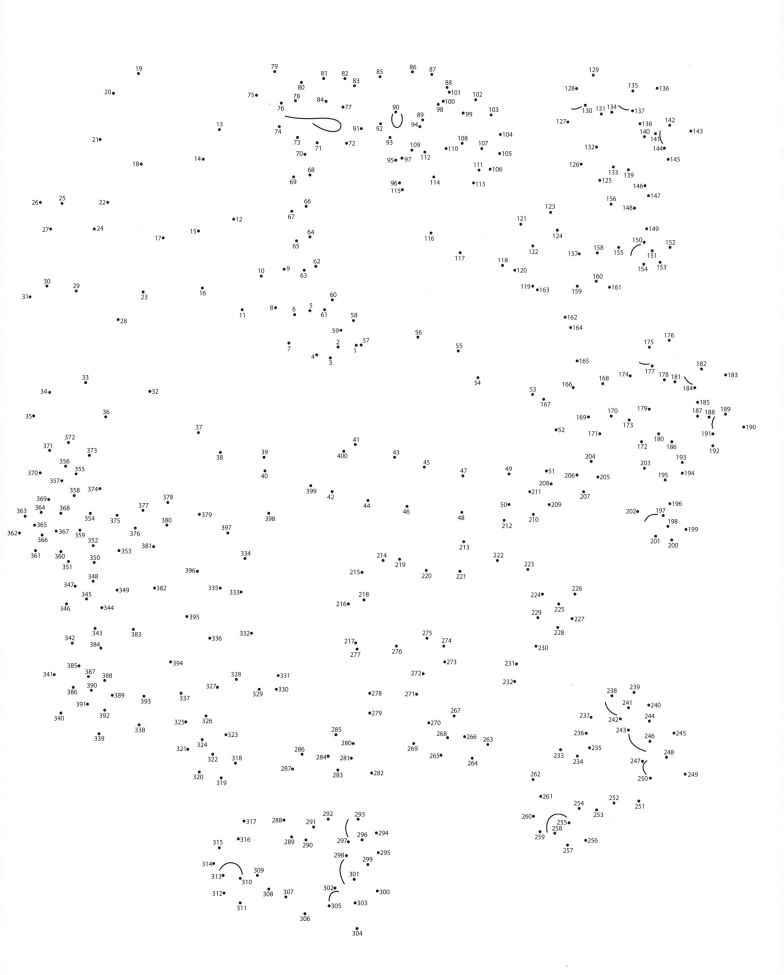

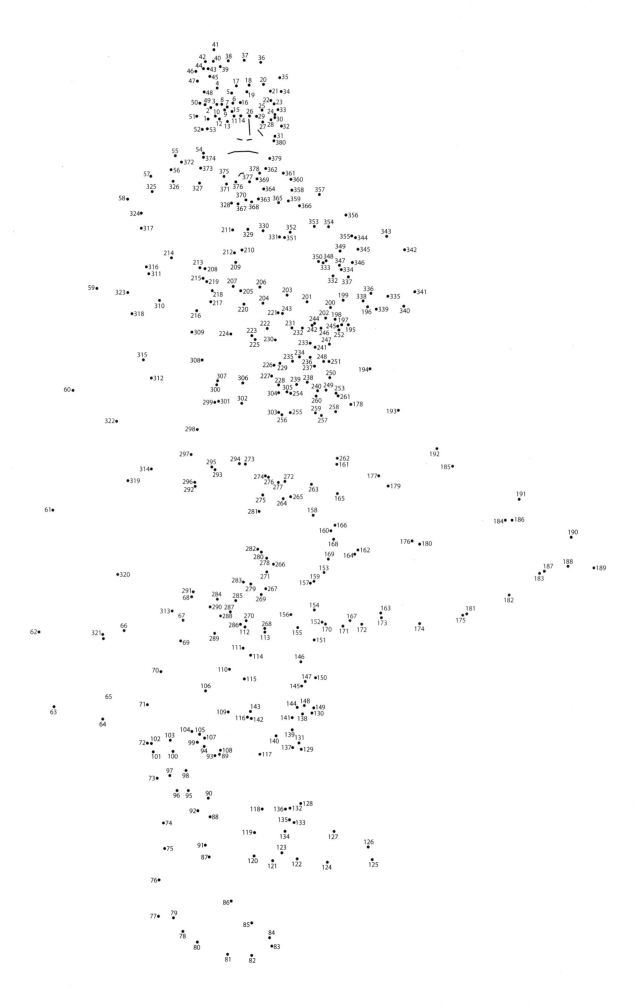

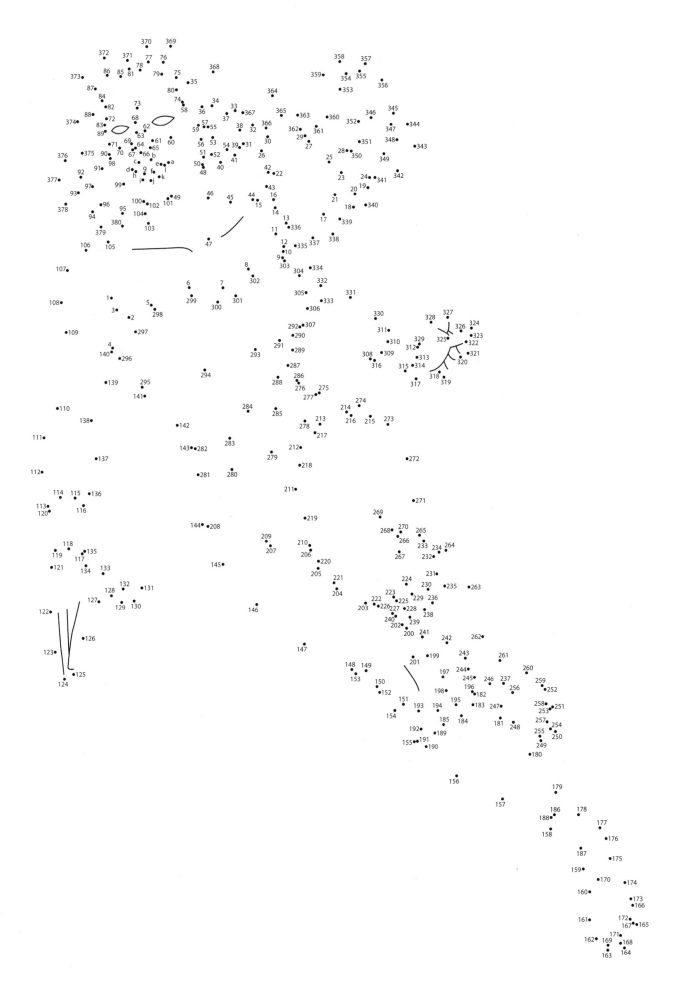

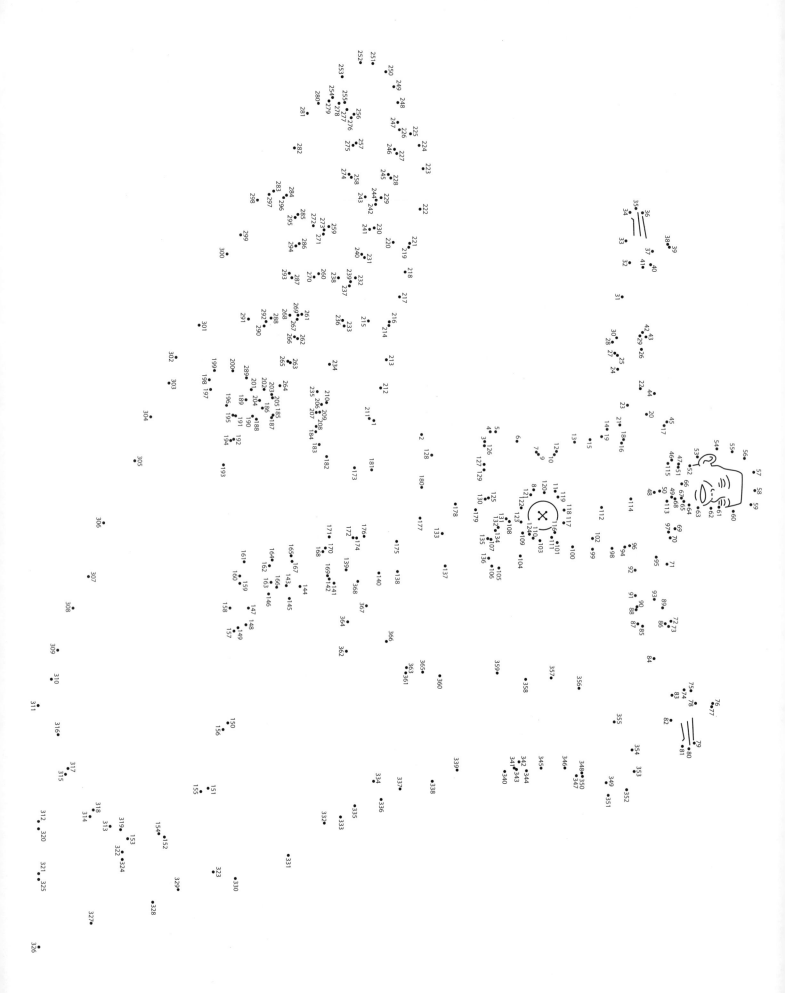

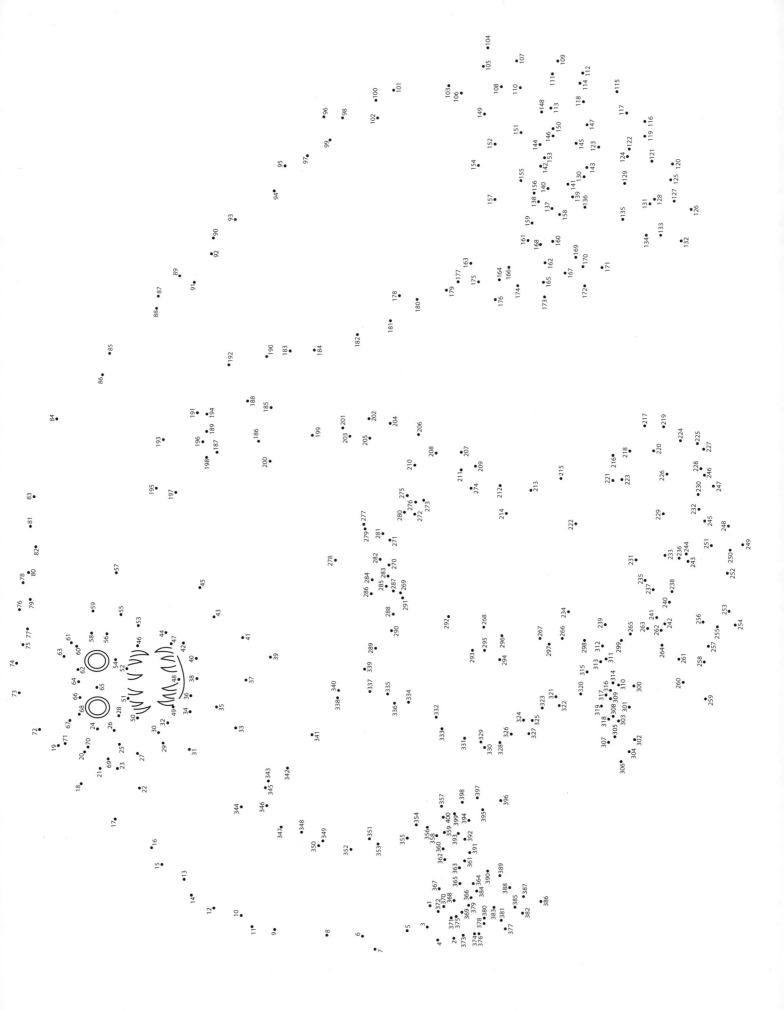

LIST OF ILLUSTRATIONS